J. F. ALDRICH

WATCH OFFICER'S GUIDE

THE WATCH OFFICER'S GUIDE

A Handbook for All Deck Watch Officers

Revised by

CAPTAIN JOHN V. NOEL, JR., U. S. NAVY

and

COMMANDER CHARLES R. CHANDLER, U. S. NAVY

Under the Technical Supervision
of the Head of the
Department of Seamanship and Navigation
U. S. Naval Academy

U. S. NAVAL INSTITUTE
ANNAPOLIS, MARYLAND
1956

Second printing of Revised Edition, March 1956
BY
U. S. Naval Institute
Annapolis, Md.

Library of Congress Card Number 55-9028

PREFACE TO THE FIFTH EDITION

"This volume is the result of an endeavor to collect and put into a compact form those details appertaining to deck duty which will be found necessary or convenient to an officer carrying on a watch." —From the preface to the original *Watch Officer's Manual*, by Ensign Charles Emerson Hovey, U.S. Navy, 1911.

The quotation above is as applicable today as it was forty-two years ago. While the art of standing an efficient deck watch, like the art of leadership, cannot be learned from books, it can be developed with experience based upon a solid foundation of facts and professional attitudes. A thoughtful study of this volume will provide a large part of that foundation.

Ensign Hovey published his manual in January, 1911. It was the first book of its kind in the American Navy, although there had long been counterparts in the British Navy. In September of the same year he was killed in action while leading a landing party ashore against outlaw Moros in the Philippines. He was cited for conspicuous gallantry in action by a General Order of the Secretary of the Navy, and a few years later a destroyer was named for him. The old four-piper U.S.S. *Hovey* is gone, but this small volume is a more lasting memorial to a promising young officer.

In 1917 the Manual was revised and enlarged by Lieutenant Solomon Endel, U.S. Navy. This second edition, published by the U.S. Naval Institute, was the last to carry Hovey's name. Shortly after World War I, the Naval Institute acquired all rights from the Hovey estate. Commander W. S. Farber, U.S. Navy, in his extensive revision of 1930 for the Naval Institute, changed the name of the third edition to *Watch Officer's Guide.* This was done to avoid confusion with the various Navy Department bureau manuals. Commander Farber's edition incorporated the most extensive changes in both format and in content and was the forerunner of the book in its modern form. In 1935 Captain Russell Willson again revised the *Watch Officer's Guide* as the fourth edition. This version, while extensively rewritten, followed the format and contents of the third edition. The Navy was beginning its great expansion, and the *Watch Officer's Guide* by Captain Willson became an important training aid for all junior officers.

In 1949 Captain F. D. McCorkle, U.S. Navy, Head of the Department of Seamanship and Navigation at the U.S. Naval Academy, instigated the current revision with the aim of including all the changes and new wrinkles resulting from the techniques and equipment developed during World War II.

The *Watch Officer's Guide,* in its present form, has been compiled and written by Commander John V. Noel, Jr., U.S. Navy, and Commander Charles R. Chandler, U.S. Navy, as an extra-departmental project.

A book of this nature must depend for its complete and authoritative coverage on the comments and recommendations of many officers. It would be impractical to list all of these persons who verbally, or in reviewing certain parts of the book, have generously contributed their time and knowledge. The list would include most of the Fleet Type Commanders, as well as officers in the Office of the Chief of Naval Operations, the Bureau of Naval Personnel, the General Line School, and the Department of Seamanship and Navigation. The important contributions of all of these officers are gratefully acknowledged.

March, 1953

M. F. D. Flaherty
Captain, U.S. Navy
Head of the Department of
Seamanship and Navigation
U.S. Naval Academy

PREFACE TO THE SIXTH EDITION

This latest revision of the standard textbook, *Watch Officer's Guide,* includes numerous changes in the section on Rules of the Nautical Road occasioned by international agreement and statutory and administrative action. In particular this revised edition incorporates changes resulting from the 1948 International Conference on Safety of Life at Sea and subsequent statutory and administrative action by the Government of the United States in connection with International Rules, Inland Rules, and Pilot Rules for vessels under the United States flag both on the high seas and in territorial waters.

The revision of the section on Rules of the Nautical Road is the work of Lieutenant Alfred Prunski, U.S. Coast Guard, and additional illustrations are by W. M. Shannon, Sp(X)CT, U.S. Naval Reserve.

December 15, 1953

John S. Lewis
Captain, U.S. Navy
Head of the Department of
Seamanship and Navigation
U.S. Naval Academy

PREFACE TO THE SEVENTH EDITION

This edition is essentially the same as the sixth with the addition of certain material on watch organization and a new chapter on the deck log. The material on organization was added to bring the *Watch Officer's Guide* more closely into consonance with *Shipboard Procedures*, NWP 50. The new chapter on writing the deck log follows the latest Navy Department directive on that subject. At the same time the entire text has been closely examined and a few relatively minor changes and additions have been made.

This seventh edition was prepared by Captain John V. Noel, Jr., U.S. Navy, assisted by Commander J. E. Reedy, U.S. Navy.

For the convenience of those who have studied the fifth or sixth edition the new material may be found on pages 8-17, 51-76, 195, and 231.

John S. Lewis
Captain, U.S. Navy
Head of the Department of
Seamanship and Navigation
U.S. Naval Academy

April, 1955

CONTENTS

PART ONE

THE GENERAL DUTIES OF THE OFFICER OF THE DECK

PART TWO

DUTIES OF THE OFFICER OF THE DECK UNDERWAY

PART FOUR

MISCELLANEOUS

PART ONE

THE GENERAL DUTIES OF THE OFFICER OF THE DECK

Chapter I

INTRODUCTION

"The commanding officer shall establish such watches as are necessary for the safety and proper operation of the command."—*U.S. Navy Regulations, 1948* (Art. 1002-1).

"The officer of the deck is the officer on watch in charge of the ship. He shall be responsible for the safety of the ship and for the performance of the duties prescribed in these regulations and by the commanding officer. Every person on board who is subject to the orders of the commanding officer, except the executive officer, and those other officers specified in Article 1009, shall be subordinate to the officer of the deck."—*U.S. Navy Regulations, 1948* (Art. 1008).

The position of the Officer of the Deck of a naval ship is unique; it has no exact parallel in the other services or in civilian life. While he is on watch the Officer of the Deck is, next to the Commanding Officer and the Executive Officer, the most important officer aboard. Under the Commanding Officer and Executive Officer he is in command of the ship as a whole. This in itself should emphasize the importance and desirability of every newly-commissioned officer becoming a qualified deck watch officer as early in his career as practicable. In no other position can a young officer so readily distinguish himself and bring himself to the favorable notice of the more senior officers aboard. Every group of ensigns newly reported to their ship will at once invite the kindly yet critical observation of their seniors. Every division officer and head of department is looking for new assistants—someone to take the A Division next quarter, perhaps, or someone to take Turret Two from Lt. Jones, who expects to be ordered to flight training. One of the best ways for a young officer to make a good beginning in his career is to stand an alert and intelligent watch. He will then naturally fall into jobs of importance and prestige, and will, at the same time, be the most unlikely candidate for the numerous and onerous routine chores that have to be done aboard ship. Standing a good watch is one of the first and most important tests that a young officer must pass in the Fleet; this book is designed to help him pass that test.

Wide Responsibility

The authority of the Officer of the Deck is matched by his responsibility; for nothing that occurs in the ship or nearby should escape his cognizance. The closing of a watertight door far below decks, the reception of a weather message in main radio, pumping of the fireroom bilges, sweeping down the main deck aft, securing an irish pennant on the muzzle bag of Number 5 gun, unfouling the commission pennant, as well as keeping the ship in formation while darkened at high speed during the night, are all matters that concern the Officer of the Deck. It is often difficult for officers to appreciate fully this broad range of their responsibilities. Their working hours are devoted to specific and specialized duties which require most of their energy and powers of concentration. Going on watch must be accepted as a radical break from usual duties. The Officer of the Deck, as he relieves the deck, must, by a deliberate and planned effort, enlarge his horizon.

Emphasis on Most Important Duties

There are two aspects of this question of broad responsibility that may profitably be discussed. The first is the matter of emphasis. Certainly the Officer of the Deck must devote himself to the important jobs first. If the ship is in formation then he is required to keep the ship on station and safe from collision even if that takes all his attention. The routine of the ship and other less important matters may properly be delegated to an assistant, either a junior officer or a petty officer.

In contrast to a situation where the Officer of the Deck must devote all his attention to one important matter, there will be occasions during a quiet watch when the Officer of the Deck can also direct his attention to the details of administration and routine of the ship. Perhaps a request is made to have the word passed, "The man who has the keys to the paint locker lay up to the paint locker." The alert Officer of the Deck will at once investigate the matter to discover why the normal and regulation methods of key custody have not been followed. It is not enough for a ship's order on keys to be written and promulgated; it must be obeyed, and the Officer of the Deck can assist in this requirement. There may be confusion, waste, and even danger if access to locked spaces is not readily available. The point here is that when nothing of great importance is happening, the Officer of the Deck can, and should, devote more attention to the routine administration of his ship as well as to the training and instruction of his watch.

The Limitations to Officer of the Deck Activities

A second aspect of the wide scope of an Officer of the Deck's responsibility is that he must not unnecessarily interfere with the duties and responsibilities of other ship's officers. While the Officer of the Deck must be sure that everything is running according to plan, he must not try to improve or revise matters unless a crisis or emergency exists. For example, an Officer of the Deck may observe that a gunnery drill is being mismanaged by one of the new ensigns. While he might discuss the matter informally then or after his watch is over, the Officer of the Deck is not expected to step in and take charge unless safety precautions are being violated or some damage to material or injury to personnel is a possibility.

Dealing with Senior Officers

One of the reasons why it is important for the Officer of the Deck to reflect at some length on the extent of his responsibility and authority is that at times he may have to exert his authority over officers *senior* to him. For example, the Supply Officer may have stores coming aboard near the quarter-deck which may interfere with the reception of an important visitor who arrives unexpectedly. The Officer of the Deck should explain to the Supply Officer the circumstances which will not permit loading stores in the vicinity of the quarter-deck. If disagreement results from this situation, the matter should be referred to the Executive Officer. The point here is that the authority of the Officer of the Deck is vested by *Navy Regulations* and by custom and usage in the *office,* not the individual *person,* of the Officer of the Deck.

How Authority Is Exerted

"He (an officer in charge of a watch) shall scrupulously obey all orders and regulations and shall require the same of all persons on watch under him.

"At all times he shall present and conduct himself in a manner befitting his office. His orders shall be issued in the customary phraseology of the service."—*U.S. Navy Regulations, 1948* (Art. 1005).

In the first part of the chapter we discussed the wide scope of the authority and the responsibility of the Officer of the Deck. Here we will treat in broad terms the manner in which this authority should be exercised. First of all, as the quotation above indicates, the Officer of the Deck must conduct his watch in a strictly regulation manner. This has nothing to do with the personal views or inclinations of the Officer of the Deck. His one duty and obligation is to carry out the orders of higher authority, be they *Navy Regulations* or the latest memorandum from the Executive Officer. In the chapters following we will discuss the different sources of directives and information with which the Officer of the Deck must be familiar. It suffices here to stress the point that the officer on watch must consider himself the dispassionate instrument by which naval doctrine, policy, and directive are implemented. From the clean white hats set squarely upon the heads of his signal gang to the departure of the 1600 liberty boat exactly on the bell, everything concerning a ship's watch should be correct, professional, and regulation. The Officer of the Deck, in his attitude and actions, represents the collective pride of the ship's company as well as the professional reputation of his Commanding Officer. A single lubberly boat coxswain, a tattered ensign not quite close up, or a signal that the ship is not in proper station may appear to be small matters in themselves, but to the Commanding Officer who has waited fifteen years for his first command they are matters of some importance. They are also of real importance to every officer and man who takes pride in his Service and in his ship.

Appeal to the Men's Pride

It is this consideration, moreover, pride in the ship, that should be emphasized. There are many small ways in which an Officer of the Deck can indicate his concern with the reputation of the ship. Men are usually quicker to react to an appeal to their pride and self respect than they are to the threat of disapproval or punishment. A lookout, a signalman, or a boat coxswain will do his work much more effectively if he wants to do a good job rather than if he is just afraid of doing a poor one. Here lies the one most obvious difference between an excellent watch and just a good or average one. For outstanding performance the men need motivation. There is nothing mysterious about how to achieve this interest and drive in the men on watch under you; the important point to understand is the necessity for it if you want to do a really good job. Later on in this book the subject of personal relations will be developed in more detail.

Other Human Factors

In this general discussion of how an Officer of the Deck exerts his authority it is enough to point out that he exerts it through people. The manner in which he deals with people is, in a large sense, a measure of his success as an Officer of the Deck.

In dealing with his seniors an officer must, of course, be tactful, alert, energetic, and resourceful. *If the Commanding Officer has strong views on certain matters which may appear to be at some variance with doctrine or with past practices, then by all means do it his way.*

In dealing with his juniors an Officer of the Deck exerts his authority with scrupulous justice and fairness. There is no room for capricious, arbitrary, or oppressive application of authority. It serves no useful purpose, for example, to become unduly exasperated with men who perform badly on watch or who appear on the quarter-deck to go on liberty in a dirty uniform. There is always a cause (although not an excuse) for this sort of behavior, and there is always someone responsible for the training and appearance of each man on board.

WATCH ORGANIZATION

The basic organization of a watch aboard ship should

be understood by all junior officers. Charts and functional guides *for the key watch officers* are the best means to accomplish this understanding. The peacetime watch organization described herein pertains to the normal peacetime watch underway (Condition IV) and in port (Condition V). It is derived from *Shipboard Procedures,* NWP 50. The material on the Command Duty Officer is included for information.

The requirements of Condition IV are:

(1) No weapons manned.

(2) Engineering plant ready for speeds as ordered.

(3) Material Condition Yoke (Baker) modified for daylight access.

(4) Surface lookout coverage. Air lookouts posted during flight operations.

(5) CIC and interior communications manned for routine purposes.

(6) Aircraft readiness as required by flight schedule.

The Command Duty Officer Underway (Functional Guide)

The Command Duty Officer is that officer eligible for command at sea who has been designated by the Commanding Officer for a particular watch for the purpose of supervising, advising, and directing the Officer of the Deck in matters concerning the general operation and safety of the ship. For the information of the Officer of the Deck his functions are listed below.

The Command Duty Officer underway shall:

(a) Keep himself informed of the tactical situation and of all factors that may affect safe navigation, such as speed, visibility, depth of water, the movements of other ships, etc.

(b) Keep himself informed concerning effective operation plans and orders, signals, intentions of the OTC (Officer in Tactical Command) and the Commanding Officer, and such other matters as concern ships or force operations.

(c) Be familiar with tactical publications, voice radio communications, procedures, recognition and authenticating procedures, and the rules of the nautical road.

(d) Keep himself informed on matters concerning the operating procedures of the ship, and advise or direct the Officer of the Deck, as required, in matters affecting the ship's operations or action.

(e) In time of danger or emergency, take command action as appropriate until the Commanding Officer or the Executive Officer arrives on the bridge and relieves the Command Duty Officer of his responsibilities.

(f) Relieve the Officer of the Deck only when required for the safety of the ship, and inform the Commanding Officer immediately when such action is taken.

While on watch, the Command Duty Officer underway has the same relationship with the Officer of the Deck as that prescribed for the Executive Officer in *U.S. Navy Regulations, 1948*.

Pertinent articles are quoted herewith:

"The executive officer may direct the officer of the deck in matters concerning the general duties and safety of the ship. When the commanding officer is not on deck, the executive officer may direct the officer of the deck how to proceed in time of danger or during an emergency, or he may assume charge of the deck himself, and shall do so should it in his judgment be necessary."—*U.S. Navy Regulations, 1948* (Art. 1009-1).

"When the commanding officer considers that circumstances warrant, he may delegate to another officer, for a specified watch, authority similar to that prescribed in the preceding paragraph for the executive officer in relation to the officer of the deck. Such officer shall, while on watch, bear the same relation to the officer of the deck both in authority and responsibility, as that prescribed for the executive officer, but shall be subordinate to the executive officer."—*U.S. Navy Regulations, 1948* (Art. 1009-2).

The Command Duty Officer in port is that officer eligible for command at sea who has been designated by the Commanding Officer as deputy to the Executive Officer for carrying out the routine of the ship in port, and for supervising and directing the Officer of the Deck in matters concerning the safety and general duties of the ship. In the temporary absence of the Executive Officer his duties will be carried out by the Command Duty Officer.

The Command Duty Officer in port shall:

(a) Advise and, if necessary, direct the Officer of the Deck in matters concerning the general activities and safety of the ship.

(b) Keep informed of the ship's position, mooring lines or ground tackle in use, the status of the engineering plant, and all other matters which affect the safety and security of the ship.

(c) In times of danger or emergency, take command action as appropriate until an officer senior to him in the succession to command relieves him.

(d) Relieve the Officer of the Deck only when necessary for the safety of the ship, and inform the Commanding Officer when such action is taken.

(e) Conduct frequent inspections to insure the security of the ship. Give particular attention to the security of the ship's boats and to the safety of personnel embarked therein.

(f) In the absence of the Executive Officer, receive the eight o'clock reports.

(g) Keep advised of routine matters affecting the internal administration of the ship.

The Officer of the Deck Underway (Functional Guide) (See Fig. 1)

In amplification of the responsibilities prescribed in Chapter 10 of *U.S. Navy Regulations, 1948,* the Officer of the Deck underway shall:

(a) Keep himself continually informed concerning the tactical situation and geographical factors which may affect the safe navigation of the ship, and take appropriate action to avoid the danger of grounding or collision in accordance with tactical doctrine, the rules of the nautical road, and the orders of the Commanding Officer or other proper authority.

(b) Keep himself informed concerning current operation plans and orders, the intentions of the OTC and the Commanding Officer, and such other matters as may pertain to ship or force operations.

(c) Issue necessary orders to the steersman and main engine control to avoid danger, to take or keep an assigned station; or to change the course and speed of the ship in accordance with orders of proper authority.

(d) Make all reports to the Commanding Officer that are required by Art. 1020, *U.S. Navy Regulations, 1948,* and by the Commanding Officer.

(e) Insure that required reports to the Officer of the Deck concerning tests and inspections, and the routine reports of patrols, watches, and lifeboat crews, are promptly originated, and that the bridge

WATCH ORGANIZATION UNDERWAY
ROUTINE STEAMING

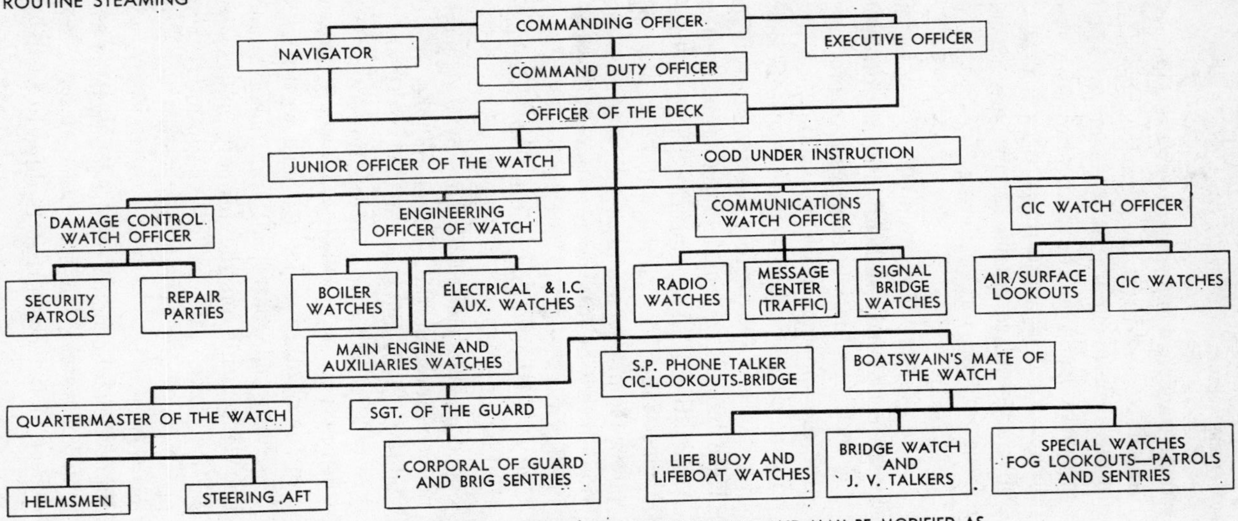

THIS CHART ILLUSTRATES THE BASIC WATCH ORGANIZATION, AND MAY BE MODIFIED AS NECESSARY TO FIT A PARTICULAR SHIP.

FIGURE 1

watch and lookouts are properly posted and alert.

(f) Supervise and direct the personnel on watch on the bridge, and insure that all required entries are properly made in the quartermaster's notebook.

(g) Prepare and sign the rough deck log, and insure that all required entries are properly made.

(h) Issue orders for rendering honors to passing vessels.

(i) Insure that the Executive Officer and department heads concerned are kept informed of changes in the tactical situation, changes in operation schedules, the approach of heavy weather, or any other circumstances which would require a change in the ship's routine or other action on their part.

(j) Keep himself informed of the status and current capabilities of the engineering plant, and keep the engineering officer of the watch advised of boiler power requirements and the physical situation topside, so that he may operate the engineering plant intelligently.

(k) Carry out the routine of the ship as published in the Plan of the Day.

(l) Supervise and control the use of the general announcing system, the general and chemical alarm, and the whistle and siren.

(m) Insure that all safety precautions are observed when men go aloft or work over the sides or traverse the weather decks in rough weather.

(n) Supervise and control all transmissions and acknowledgements on the primary and secondary tactical voice radio circuits, and insure that proper phraseology and procedure are used in all transmissions.

(o) Supervise and conduct on-the-job training for personnel on watch.

The Officer of the Deck reports directly to the Commanding Officer for the safe navigation and general operation of the ship, and to the Executive Officer for carrying out the ship's routine.

The following personnel report to the Officer of the Deck:

(a) The Junior Officer of the Watch and the Officer of the Deck under instruction, for the performance of their duties and for on-watch training.

(b) The Combat Information Center Watch Officer for the conduct of air and surface radar search and tracking, for supplying combat and tactical information affecting the maneuvering and safe navigation of the ship, and for conducting visual air and surface search.

(c) The Engineering Officer of the Watch for the speed and direction of rotation of the main engines.

(d) The Communication Watch Officer for accurate and rapid transmission and receipt of visual tactical and general information signals, and for other communications affecting the operation or maneuvering of the ship.

(e) The damage control watch (patrols) for the reporting and control of hull damage and casualties, and for the setting and maintenance of prescribed material conditions.

The Officer of the Deck in Port (Functional Guide) (See Fig. 2)

The Officer of the Deck in port shall:

(a) Keep continually informed of the ship's position, mooring lines or ground tackle in use, tide and weather information, the status of the engineering plant, the status of the ship's boats, and all other matters affecting the safety and security of the ship, and take appropriate action to prevent grounding, collision, dragging or other danger.

WATCH ORGANIZATION IN PORT

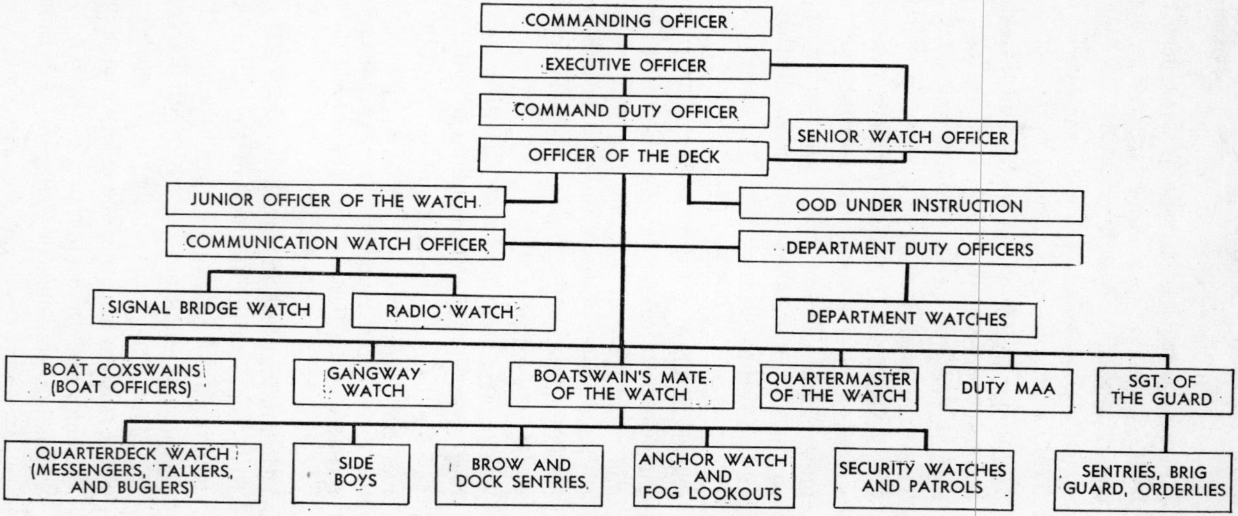

FIGURE 2

(b) Insure that required reports to the Officer of the Deck concerning tests and inspections, and the routine reports of patrols, watches, and sentries, are promptly originated, and that the quarterdeck watch, lookouts, anchor watch, and other sentries or patrols are properly posted and alert.
(c) Prepare and sign the rough deck log, and insure that all required entries are made in the quartermaster's notebook.
(d) Insure that the Executive Officer, Command Duty Officer, and department heads are informed of any circumstances which would require a change in the ship's routine or other action on their part.
(e) Carry out the ship's routine.
(f) Attend one of the ship's gangways, and supervise those watch personnel assigned to other gangways.
(g) Supervise and direct the ship's boats safely and expeditiously.
(h) Supervise and control the use of the general announcing system, the general and chemical alarm, and the whistle and siren.
(i) Insure that all safety precautions are observed when men go aloft or work over the side.
(j) Make all required reports to the Commanding Officer.
(k) Supervise and conduct on-the-job training for personnel of the quarterdeck watch.

QUALIFICATIONS OF AN OFFICER OF THE DECK

Forehandedness

It is not humanly possible to be at all times letter perfect in everything that may concern an Officer of the Deck. The superior watch officer, however, is always ready for any situation that may arise, and for that reason, if we assume normal personal and professional qualifications, the most important faculty to be cultivated by the Officer of the Deck is that of *forehandedness*. If the prospects are that you may have fog in your watch, check over the fog procedure before taking the deck. If you are to take part in Fleet Exercises, arrange to look over the orders before going on watch. If you are to enter New York harbor, review the Inland Rules of the Road. If your watch is to be full of ceremonies, be letter perfect in the honors required, and put a little extra snap in your own appearance. Always look ahead, a minute, an hour, or a day, and make it your pride never to be caught unprepared. Rehearse mentally the action you would take in the event of a fire, a man overboard, a steering failure, or any other serious casualty. This habit is not difficult to acquire and is certain to pay large dividends over the course of years. *Forehandedness* is the mark of the successful man in any administrative capacity.

Vigilance

Next to forehandedness in being thoroughly prepared for conditions and circumstances that may reasonably be expected during your watch, the most important quality for the Officer of the Deck is probably *vigilance*. In no position more than that of Officer of the Deck is "eternal vigilance the price of safety." The Officer of the Deck must, of course, observe intelligently all that comes within his vision, both outside and inside the ship, but his vigilance must extend beyond this. He must cultivate the faculty of "foreseeing" situations as well as seeing them, and must maintain and develop the vigilance of all others concerned with his watch. A recent instruction issued by Commander Amphibious Force, Atlantic Fleet, contained the following significant paragraph: "Training in mental alertness is a continuous process. It cannot be restricted to potentially dangerous situations. The daily routine and activities aboard a man-of-war provide numerous opportunities for such training. The same type of mental lethargy which will permit an Officer of the Deck to stand abreast a lighted gangway after sunrise, or a signal watch to be oblivious to a flag hoist or visual call, will permit a boat at the boom to slowly fill with water and sink, or will fail to detect in time an incipient collision."

Common Sense

A third important quality for the successful Officer of the Deck is that of *common sense,* which in his position is largely a sense of proportion and of the fitness of things. Watches vary all the way from hours of tenseness where your ship and shipmates are in your hands every instant, as in high-speed work at night in a darkened ship, down to the calm of a quiet Sunday afternoon at anchor, when you are just "keeping ship." It is well to adjust to the kind of watch. On the darkened destroyer, only essentials count and you must key your mind to its keenest pitch. On the Sunday afternoon, while there is no excuse for slackness, it may be that your most important immediate responsibility is to be affable and agreeable to undistinguished visitors.

Appearance and Manner

The fourth important quality is largely a question of *appearance and manner;* but it is more than mere smartness, it is a manifestation of *leadership,* the exemplification of which instills in subordinates confidence, pride, and a desire to emulate. Every watch officer should cultivate dignity, force, confidence, and precision in his manner of standing watch, and should exact similar qualities from his assistants. He should be careful of his personal appearance, and should strive to avoid any indication of confusion, peevishness, or noisiness. He should always act the part of what he really is—next to the Captain and the Executive Officer, the most important person in the ship.

Technical Knowledge

The Officer of the Deck, no matter how well endowed with forehandedness, vigilance, common sense, and a military appearance, must have more—he must have technical knowledge of his job; he must know the relative importance of his many responsibilities; and he must have experience. This book cannot cover even briefly the field of technical knowledge required by the Officer of the Deck, nor can it furnish him with experience; it attempts, however, in the following pages to indicate:

The sources of technical knowledge with which a watch officer must be familiar

The relative importance of the watch officer's many responsibilities

The lessons of accumulated experience so far as they can be reproduced in the printed page

Certain convenient information which otherwise might not be readily available when wanted.

Chapter II

THE WATCH IN GENERAL

"He (the officer of the deck) shall remain in charge and at his station until regularly relieved. He shall scrupulously obey all orders and regulations and shall require the same of all persons on watch under him. He shall instruct them as may be necessary in the performance of their duties, and shall insure that they are at their stations, attentive, alert, and ready for duty. He shall endeavor to foresee situations which may arise, and shall take such timely and remedial action as may be required.

"Before relieving, he shall thoroughly acquaint himself with all matters which he should know for the proper performance of his duties while on watch. He may decline to relieve his predecessor should any circumstances or situation exist which, in his opinion, justifies such action by him, until he has reported the facts to and received orders from the commanding officer, or other competent authority."—*U.S. Navy Regulations, 1948* (Art. 1005).

PREPARATION

This chapter will be devoted to the preparation for, and the conduct of, a deck watch. It will cover, in general terms, those matters common to both watches in port and those underway. Subsequent chapters will deal separately and in detail with the distinctive features of port and underway watches.

The more thorough your preparation before going on watch, the more likely you are to perform your duties efficiently. The problem really has two aspects. You need general indoctrination in all the characteristics of the ship and her crew before you can stand a useful watch; and you also require, under certain conditions, a good deal of exact local information before you relieve the deck.

Let us discuss the first aspect. Assuming that you are reporting to your first ship or have been ordered to one that is unfamiliar, you need to know a great deal about the ship itself: its organization, and the people who run it. Most of this you will have to dig out for yourself. You will normally be provided with a copy of the ship's organization book, including notices and instructions. This can be quite an indigestible item, especially in a large ship, if you attempt to learn the whole thing. It is better to learn the skeleton first, then concentrate on the parts that will affect you the most. Usually you will be rewarded by gaining a reasonably clear picture of who does what, where, and when. If, unfortunately, you are in a ship that has no written organization that is followed, you can only resolve to learn your ship the hard way. You might resolve, at the same time, that when you fleet up to positions of responsibility you will have the good sense either to follow the ship's written organization or else to write a new one to met your special needs. Running a ship on the verbal directives of a few strong personalities is much like playing the piano by ear—it works, after a fashion, but is not really professional.

It is difficult to overemphasize the importance of your ship's organization book. It is the key to the proper administration of the ship. It is the single most useful reference an officer has aboard ship and his best guide in learning how the ship functions.

The other major source of information about your ship will be found in the Damage Control Officer's office. Booklets of general plans and casualty control bills will enable you to acquire the over-all knowledge of the ship's compartmentation, fittings, piping, and wiring that an Officer of the Deck should have.

Of course, you may be put on the watch list almost immediately upon reporting. This is often standard procedure, since the junior officer watch list is never long enough to suit anyone; and besides, there is much that you can learn only by doing. When this happens you can be sure that you will be a Junior Officer of the Watch (JOOW) and will not be expected to assume important responsibilities at first. See the check-off list at the end of this chapter for a useful guide in starting to learn your ship.

There is another kind of information that an Officer of the Deck requires before relieving the watch: this is a knowledge of the immediate situation—tactical, if underway; usually administrative, if not underway. These subjects will be covered in subsequent chapters.

There are a few other aspects of being prepared to stand a watch that should be mentioned. In view of the importance of the watch to you personally and, under certain circumstances, to the safety of your shipmates, it should be considered an obligation on the part of every officer to be in good physical shape before going on watch. This means being reasonably well rested, if that is within your power to accomplish. While it often happens that you must relieve the watch—for example, the 2000-2400—when you are dog-tired after a day of gunnery exercises that began at dawn, there are other times when you can relax for an hour or so before going on duty. You usually have a choice before the midwatch, for example, whether or not to turn in for a few hours.

If you have a minor ailment, such as a bad cold, do not hesitate to ask the senior watch officer for a relief if you do not feel that you can meet the demands of a difficult watch.

RELIEVING THE WATCH

There are only two ways to relieve the watch: the correct way and the wrong way. Since the correct way is also the most efficient way, we will discuss it in some detail. The first thing to remember is to *get up on deck early*. You need time to read the message board, check the log of the last watch, visit Combat Information Center (CIC) if the situation warrants, and gather all possible information that you will need. Not later than fifteen minutes before the hour you should step up to the officer you are relieving, salute him, and say: "I am ready to relieve you, sir." Aside from the obvious aspects of this formality, such as setting an example of smartness and military courtesy for the men and observing a time honored custom of the Service, there are very sound reasons for this procedure. The key word is *ready*. By declaring yourself ready to relieve the watch you are stating that you have made all reasonable preparations, gathered all available information, and need but an oral turnover to assume your duties. A mumbled "What's the dope?" is not an acceptable substitute. It is more than a matter of good manners, it is an obligation to the shipmate whom you are to succeed on watch, to say: "I am ready to relieve you, sir."

As you receive information about the watch you have an opportunity to observe what is going on, both aboard ship and outside the ship. When you thoroughly understand the situation and have heard all that your predecessor has to say and have asked him any questions you may think necessary, it is again your duty to salute him and say: "I relieve you, sir." It must be stressed that this is an obligation and must not be done with a sloppy "O.K., I've got it." Taking over a watch is serious business and must be done in a clearcut, positive, seamanlike manner.

WHEN NOT TO RELIEVE THE WATCH

It might be useful here to discuss the problem that sometimes arises when a conscientious officer feels that he must decline to relieve the deck. The extracts from *Navy Regulations* quoted at the beginning of this chapter are quite clear on this subject. There is often a feeling among junior officers, however, that they may be considered timid if they exercise their option and decline to relieve the deck. This feeling is not warranted. It is an officer's duty to decline to relieve the deck if, for example, the ship is out of position in the formation or if a busy watch in port has become somewhat confused, with boats astray or out of fuel. Of course, reasonable judgment must be exercised. A ship may be out of position for good reason and be headed back for her station. It would then be quite proper to relieve the deck. In general, however, a careful, meticulous approach to this question is recommended. An old salt has said: "Relieve in haste, repent at leisure." A reputation for being fussy in taking over a watch is not a bad thing to acquire. It will often keep your predecessor on his toes, ready to turn over his watch with no loose ends to embarrass you. Remember that after you have said: "I relieve you, sir," the full responsibility of the watch is *yours*. It will never do then to try to pass the blame back to the officer you relieved if difficulties arise.

ORGANIZING THE WATCH

The most logical way to regard the people on watch under you is to look upon them as a team whose success will depend on their organization (teamwork), individual capabilities, morale, and the plays you call for them.

Organization comes first and, of course, requires that every man know the extent of his responsibilities. Never assume, in taking over a watch, that *all* your billets are filled by men who know what they are doing. Even the best of ship's organizations will slip a cog at times and the result may be a weak spot on your team. Check your key personnel; be sure that they know their job. If in doubt, have them instructed or backed up by one of the old hands. In extreme cases it may be necessary to have a man relieved by someone better qualified.

It is easier to organize and run your watch efficiently if you know, in general, the duties of the men under you. The various Navy training courses for different rates and ratings are obvious (yet much neglected) sources of information. These well written, compact, little blue paper-bound books are crammed with useful information. Much of it is not readily available even in other Navy publications. For example, the boatswain's mate course books contain detailed instructions for the boatswain's mate on watch. A reasonable familiarity with these details will greatly assist you in supervising your watch.

You have an opportunity, when organizing your watch, to exercise forehandedness. While underway, for example, you can instruct your lookouts to be alert to sight a particular ship or point of land. Word of anticipated changes in speed can be passed down to the engine-room. If your ship is in port, the signal bridge can be alerted to inform you of the approach of expected visitors. By keeping your men informed you stimulate their interest and invariably increase their efficiency.

It is a good idea to check your quartermasters not only to be sure that they are keeping the proper records such as weather data, compass record book, bearing book, etc., but also to insure that they are keeping notes properly in the quartermaster's log. Although this log is kept in pencil, it is an official Navy record and entries must never be erased. During a busy watch it is advisable to see that sufficient entries are being made in the quartermaster's log to enable you to write your own log easily and thoroughly.

THE BOATSWAIN'S MATE OF THE WATCH

"The officer of the deck shall carry out promptly and precisely the established routine and any special orders for the ship, weather and other circumstances permitting, and shall report any deviation therefrom to the commanding officer or executive officer, as appropriate. He shall follow, as practicable, the motions of the senior officer present in carrying out routine evolutions."—*U.S. Navy Regulations, 1948* (Art. 1012).

An important member of your team is the boatswain's mate of the watch. He is your principal enlisted assistant and should be made to feel responsible for the instruction, behavior, and appearance of the men under him. He should see that all stations are manned and that the previous watch has been relieved. One of his major duties is to follow the Plan of the Day in regard to routine. He must know what is happening on board ship and must pass the word in accordance with the prescribed routine. Most ships have a standard routine written into the ship's organization book which is varied only by specific instructions in the mimeographed Plan of the Day. It is the duty of the Officer of the Deck to see that the routine is followed, and his boatswain's mate should do it under his supervision. Sometimes it may seem advisable to recommend a change in the routine when unusual and unforeseen circumstances arise. In that event an Officer of the Deck always checks first with the Executive Officer or the Command Duty Officer, and obtains permission. As in most other aspects of his job, the Officer of the Deck can exercise forehandedness in carrying out the routine. If a working party is delayed in returning to the ship, for example, dinner should be saved for them as well as for the boat's crew. A good boatswain's mate will take care of such items but, unless you delegate the duty to the Junior Officer of the Watch, the job of supervising the boatswain's mate in carrying out the routine must be an important part of your duty as Officer of the Deck.

PASSING THE WORD

"His (the officer of the deck's) orders shall be issued in the customary phraseology of the service."—*U.S. Navy Regulations, 1948* (Art. 1005).

Not only must the ship's routine be followed, but the manner in which it is accomplished, the manner in which the word is passed, is most important. Often a ship will reveal to anyone within earshot how badly or how well it is being run by the manner in which the general announcing system is used. A noisy uproar every few minutes, passing the word for this person and that person, with each message obviously being composed on the spot by an enthusiastic boatswain's mate, is a sure indication of a sloppy ship. In contrast, the sparing use of the general announcing system, with only important words being passed—and those in a seamanlike manner, using the customary phraseology of the Service—is the trademark of a smart, taut ship. The Officer of the Deck himself should grant permission on each occasion for passing the word. He may give the boatswain's mate blanket permission to pass all words relating to the ship's routine. He should make sure, however, that a standard, approved terminology is used. Such expressions as "chow down" or "crew of the whaleboat, man your boat and come alongside" must not be tolerated. The list of commonly used expressions in Chapter IX is a good guide. If in doubt on terminology, consult a dictionary or glossary of naval terms or a pertinent Bureau of Naval Personnel training publication.

In passing the word, other than for the ship's routine, the Officer of the Deck should make every effort to curtail the use of the general announcing system. It is not proper to pass the word for individuals or for small groups unless there is a real emergency. If permitted, this practice of passing the word for everyone leads to abuse; no one takes the trouble to look for anyone, and inadequate supervision of the men by their officers and petty officers is abetted. The continuous chatter emerging from the loudspeaker tends to numb the audio-perception of all hands, and as a result no one really listens to the general announcing system even when important words are being passed.

An additional precaution in using the system is to be sure that only the desired circuits are cut in. Passing "sweepers" over the officers circuit, for example, is an unnecessary annoyance to those in officers country. When in port it is often advisable to reduce the volume of the weather-deck speakers, since there is no point in harassing people in other ships, on the pier, or ashore.

A word about the boatswain's pipe (originally termed a *call*). Its use should be encouraged. It serves a useful and distinctive purpose and is one of the small but important factors that comprise the ceremony and the true nautical flavor of the Navy afloat.

APPEARANCE OF THE WATCH

> "At all times he (the officer of the deck) shall present and conduct himself in a manner befitting his office."—*U.S. Navy Regulations, 1948* (Art. 1005).

The Officer of the Deck, circumstances permitting, must see that his watch is in clean and regulation uniform, and that the bridge or quarter-deck is orderly and neat. This starts with the Officer of the Deck himself, who sets an example, at all times, for the whole ship. At sea, and in bad weather particularly, he should be dressed to keep warm and dry and should see that his men on watch are similarly protected. In port, with visitors coming aboard, the maximum of spit and polish is expected. Uniforms in good condition, polished shoes, and clean white hats are in order. Make the boatswain's mate of the watch responsible for the appearance of the watch, and do not hesitate to send men below to change who are not up to your standards. Old, patched undress blues or soiled work shoes are good enough to wear about the deck, but are not good enough for a messenger watch on the quarter-deck.

Similarly, the appearance of the bridge or quarter-deck should be a matter of interest to the Officer of the Deck. A properly run watch will keep their area picked up and clean. Sweeping the deck, emptying trash buckets and ash trays, and sending the dirty wardroom coffee cups below are all details that an alert Junior Officer of the Watch should see that his enlisted assistants attend to.

CONDUCT ON WATCH

It would be obvious and repetitious to stress here the need for decorous and seamanlike behavior on the part of all those on watch. But there is one aspect of this subject that may escape you. It is the need for a certain formality while on watch. This does not mean that you must be pompous or stuffy; there are many occasions when humor and laughter are quite appropriate. It means, however, that the men on watch must never be permitted to forget that they are on duty and that what they are doing is important. On watch, if telling sea stories or gossiping interferes with the ship's business, then it should not be permitted. A ship is always subject to emergency or disaster; fire, man overboard, or dozens of other events can disrupt the dullest watch. In making it a practice to run a taut watch and to prevent noisy and idle chatter during his watch, the Officer of the Deck must, of course, use common sense and not be arbitrary or harsh in dealing with his men. The signal gang, for example, puts in long hours on the bridge and should be permitted to relax when not busy, so long as they maintain the necessary lookout.

TURNING OVER THE WATCH

As a watch draws to a close, the Officer of the Deck is concerned with giving his relief all available information in order to provide the maximum continuity. One means to insure good turnover is to keep notes on major events during your watch with a view to giving these rough notes to your relief. Another is to use a check-off list. Remember that even while turning over the watch, you must continue to be alert and on the job. Do not let turning over distract you.

After being relieved (underway), make the following report to the Commanding Officer and the Command Duty Officer (if assigned): "I have been properly relieved, sir. Mr. —— has the deck."

THE OFFICER OF THE DECK IN AN AIRCRAFT CARRIER

In an aircraft carrier the Officer of the Deck will meet some situations not encountered in other ships. Flight operations themselves greatly complicate the routine of the ship. The very size of a large carrier, for example, makes efficient administration difficult unless the ship is skillfully organized. Men may have long distances to travel between their duty stations and their berthing and eating spaces.

In large carriers the Officer of the Deck is supported by an Assistant Officer of the Deck as well as a Junior Officer of the Watch. The latter usually handles routine matters underway, such as passing the word, mast reports, dumping trash, etc. The Assistant Officer of the Deck handles tactical circuits and relays information between the Commanding Officer and the Officer of the Deck when the noise level is high. (A piece of plexiglass and a grease pencil for a written message is often a help when the aircraft noise is so intense that you cannot be heard.) The Officer of the Deck is, of course, in general charge and usually has the conn.

There is a real necessity for the non-flying line officer who stands deck watches on a carrier to become familiar with certain aspects of the problems concerning aircraft. Some of these are:

Aircraft turn-ups and tune-ups, with the attendant safety precautions

Operation of aircraft elevators and hangar-bay doors

Operation of the helicopters

Cooperation between the gunnery department and the air department in the matter of respotting aircraft and boats

Special need for smoking discipline during gassing and degassing of aircraft, tractors, helicopters, etc.

Plane crash procedure, and the use of rescue destroyers and the need for keeping them informed

Special restrictions on blowing tubes (never during launching and recovery, and never when soot may blow over flight deck)

Special wind and weather information needed before flight operations

Limiting and optimum wind velocities and direction over the deck, with time needed to accelerate to desired speeds

Messing of air group and air department personnel before, after, and during flight operations

Need to inform air department of high winds expected so aircraft may be secured.

A CHECK-OFF LIST FOR NEW OFFICERS OF THE DECK

Here is a partial list of what the Officer of the Deck should know about his ship:

Length, beam, draft, displacement

General structural characteristics, particularly in regard to watertight integrity

Height of eye at bridge; distance to horizon at this height

Fuel oil capacity; endurance at high, medium, low speed

Speed on different boiler combinations

Time to get additional boilers on the line

Acceleration and deceleration characteristics (general)

Speeds at which superheaters are lighted off; are secured

Nature, capabilities, limitations of ship's armament

Normal daily consumption of water; evaporator capacity

Number of degrees for standard and full rudder

Tactical diameter at standard and at full rudder

How to turn ship in shortest time; in least space

Location on bridge of all ship control gear; general characteristics of such gear

Location of and facilities at other conning stations

Location and use of all equipment on bridge and in pilothouse (both daylight and dark)

Alarms to be sounded and procedure to be followed in event of fire, fire and rescue, man overboard, collision

Alarm and procedure to be followed in event of collision

Alarm and procedure to be followed in event of general quarters

Capacity and location of boats, life rafts, etc.

How to release life rafts
How to drop an anchor, veer anchor chain, operate anchor windlass
How to use a drift lead
How to lower and hoist a boat
Safety precautions for men fueling, handling ammunition, working over the side, aloft, in closed compartments, using power tools
How to set depth charges (if carried) on safe
Stations that make up special sea detail
Procedure for steering casualty
How to steer from other steering stations; and without power
Need for blowing tubes
How to detect a gyro error
How to tell if ship is dragging, and what precautions to take
How to check mooring lines
How to instruct boat coxswains in handling boats in bad weather
Equipment carried in ship's boats
How make preparations to receive a ship that will moor alongside
How make preparations to fuel, receive stores or ammunition while underway
Procedure for getting ship underway, for replenishment
Procedure in fueling boats
Preparations to be made when entering or leaving port
What publications are kept on the bridge; in CIC
Precautions in handling classified publications on the bridge
General contents of all ship's notices and instructions and of the ship's organization book
How to use visual recognition signals

Capabilities and limitations of CIC
How to use CIC, and obligation for keeping CIC informed
Characteristics, limitations, and use of all electronic equipment
How to use bridge radar repeater
What principal radio circuits are normally manned
Own ship's voice radio call and those of immediate superiors and other units in company
Organization of condition watches; what armament manned
Nature and use of principal interior communication circuits
Damage control organization, what closures are made; relation of GM to roll of ship
Operational and administrative organization of which your ship is a part
Action to be taken if required to conduct search and/or rescue
How and when to dispose of trash and/or garbage
When to pump bilges; when to blow tubes
Characteristics of aircraft carried, how to receive helicopter.

Chapter III

GENERAL NOTES FOR THE OFFICER OF THE DECK

The topics discussed herein are of a general nature that pertain to both the underway and the in-port watches of an Officer of the Deck.

PERSONNEL

"The opportunities which you, as an officer of the United States Navy, have to train and mold future citizens of the United States, future naval officers and enlisted men, are unlimited. Your responsibility is accordingly great. I expect every officer in the U.S. Atlantic Fleet to accept this responsibility as a trust, and to discharge it with complete devotion and energy."—Admiral L. D. McCormick, U.S.N.

Just as the Officer of the Deck has special responsibilities and duties concerning the ship itself and her machinery, so does he have certain special responsibilities in his dealings with the ship's company. Some of these responsibilities as regard officers have been discussed in an early chapter.

Performance

Most important, perhaps, to an Officer of the Deck is the performance of the men on duty with him. They must respond quickly and intelligently to his orders. Also, while on duty and on watch, a moderate degree of formality should be preserved. Call your Junior Officer of the Watch "Mr. Jones," not "Red-dog" or "Mike." Learn the names of the men on watch and use them. When giving an order or command it is proper to address a man on watch by his last name or by his title, such as quartermaster. Discourage conversation of the entertainment variety, particularly between officers and men on watch. This may sound unnecessarily stern, but following a policy of strict attention to duty will always pay off in the long run.

The principle of reserve and decorum on the bridge and quarter-deck applies, of course, in both directions. You may know the Navigator well enough to call him by his first name on the golf course, but call him "Mister" when you have the deck. A meticulous separation of social or personal affairs from the important business of watch standing is a good rule to follow.

Training

Another aspect of watch standing that should be considered is training. An important indoctrination that men receive in the Navy is on-the-job training—learning while they are doing. A normal watch, and particularly a quiet and uneventful one, offers many opportunities to train the men in their own duties and even in other jobs with which they should be familiar. By the exercise of a little ingenuity on the part of the Officer of the Deck, even the dullest watch can be made interesting and worthwhile. Lookouts can take a trick at the wheel, the quartermaster can teach the boatswain's mate some navigation, the boatswain's mate can drill the side boys in sound-powered telephone voice procedure, etc.

An especially important part of indoctrination and training is that given to new men reporting aboard for duty. The Officer of the Deck can play a vital part in giving the new men a good first impression. Check to see that they are provided at the earliest possible moment with bunks and lockers and are assigned to a division. Arrange a conducted tour of the ship for the new men;

they will be of little use either in work, or in an emergency, such as fire, until they know their way around. A well-administered ship has detailed plans ready for receiving new men; the Officer of the Deck is responsible for starting this procedure.

Liberty Parties

The Officer of the Deck in port is responsible for getting men off on liberty on time and after a thorough inspection. This inspection should not be perfunctory. Men going on liberty must be in clean, regulation uniforms, with hair cut, beards shaved, shoes shined. The reputation of your ship as well as the Navy depends on, among other things, the appearance of the men ashore. Men that have slight deficiencies should be warned; those who definitely fail to pass inspection should be directed to go below and correct their shortcomings. Be firm but fair; a moderately worn uniform, if clean and pressed, for example, should pass, while a new pair of shoes, dull and dusty, should not.

The return of liberty parties may be a routine matter or, under different circumstances, may be quite a lively occasion. Under normal conditions the Officer of the Deck has only to identify the men and see that their liberty cards are collected. If the ship has just made its first port after a long stretch at sea, or if the ship is sailing the next day for an extended absence, there are quite likely to be a few celebrants. This calls for a master-at-arms or corporal of the guard at the gangway to usher the men off the quarter-deck and persuade them to turn in below quietly. The Officer of the Deck must remain aloof from any confusion that may arise and should let his experienced assistants on duty handle matters. Of course, persistent rowdies or trouble makers may require your special attention, but do not speak to or admonish the men directly; act through your assistants. The men who are most in need of your attention are those who are brought aboard apparently drunk. Have these men taken to sick bay and examined; they may have head injuries or be drugged instead of, or in addition to, being drunk. If necessary, arouse the Medical Officer and have him make the examinations. Matters of this sort must be recorded fully in the log, together with the written report of medical examination.

While juniors in the Navy normally embark in boats and vehicles before their seniors, there is at least one occasion when this rule should be reversed. When embarking liberty parties into boats or busses, allow the Chief Petty Officers to go first, followed by the other petty officers in descending order of rank. This practice will enhance the prestige of the petty officers and provide a convenience which they well deserve. Also, in large ships with many officers waiting to go ashore, it may be necessary to limit the number of junior officers embarking in order to insure room for the senior officers.

Working Parties

The Officer of the Deck may often activate large working parties and require the men to complete, without rest, an important evolution such as provisioning ship. These matters are normally accepted by the men with reasonable understanding. There are many times, however, when small groups are involved, that the Officer of the Deck can contribute to the well-being of the crew by exercising forehandedness, good judgment, and consideration for the men's comfort. The men's leisure time and meal hours should be respected as much as possible. Men who are working hard through meal times should not be required to shift into another uniform just for the meal and should have complete and hot meals saved for them if they miss the regular one. Working parties leaving the ship should be provided with such comforts as rain gear, drinking water, etc., when circumstances warrant. Aside from all the more altruistic aspects, a considerate attitude on the part of the Officer of the Deck will result in more and better work on the part of the crew.

SAFETY*

"The officer of the deck shall insure that necessary measures and precautions are taken to prevent accidents. Particular care shall be exercised in heavy weather, and when men are working aloft, over the side, or in confined spaces, and when inflammables and explosives, or any other dangerous materials are being handled. Means for recovery of persons falling overboard shall be available and ready for instant use.

"Before turning over the main engines by power when not underway, the officer of the deck shall ascertain that it is safe to do so and that competent persons are stationed to give and execute the necessary signals; and he shall then obtain permission from the commanding officer."—*U.S. Navy Regulations, 1948* (Art. 1014).

Safety is an active, vital concept that should influence most of the activities of an Officer of the Deck. Going to sea and working with powerful machinery and high explosives is a dangerous business. Many of the men are young and inclined to be careless, if not downright reckless. It is an officer's responsibility in the service to combat carelessness and to protect the lives of his men.

This section will deal with safety precautions in general terms. It is not possible to list here all precautions an Officer of the Deck may have to employ. Even *U.S. Navy Safety Regulations* does not include *all* the safety precautions. This chapter will list some of the more common

* See Chapter 18, *Shipboard Procedures.*

ones and provide references where more detailed and specific safety instructions may be found.

The most obvious precaution to take to prevent loss of life through drowning is to require men to wear life jackets. This is so obvious that it is often taken for granted, yet drownings occur every year. Men are lost in swamped boats or fall over the side, and the reason for their death is sadly familiar—someone failed to insure that life jackets were worn. The Officer of the Deck, the shore patrol petty officer ashore, or the senior officer in the boat (or boat officer) must direct the use of life jackets whenever there is a real possibility of swamping or collision. All boats carry life jackets; it is merely a matter of responsibility and initiative on the part of officers or petty officers to see that the men put them on. Men working over the side are often understandably reluctant to wear a bulky kapok jacket that is hot and uncomfortable and that restricts their motions. In general, all men working over the side should wear life jackets. Even expert swimmers have drowned because they suffered injury before or during their fall. There are other occasions, such as men working or standing watch topside in heavy weather, that require the use of life jackets. The important point is for the Officer of the Deck to be alert to the danger of drowning and for him to take action.

Another common shipboard hazard is a closed compartment which may have insufficient oxygen to support life or which may be filled with explosive or poisonous vapors. The *Bureau of Ships Manual* directs that no person shall enter any closed compartment or poorly ventilated space unless and until a qualified person has indicated that the applicable directions have been complied with, and that the danger of poisoning or suffocation, or ignition of flammable gases, has been eliminated. It follows then that the Officer of the Deck, before granting permission to enter certain spaces, must make sure that a qualified person has made the tests required and specified in the *Bureau of Ships Manual.* In the event that a casualty does occur, it is important not to compound the tragedy by permitting courageous but foolhardy shipmates to go to the rescue without proper equipment. It is sometimes forgotten that a gas mask provides no oxygen, and that only a man properly equipped with rescue breathing gear should be allowed to enter a compartment that lacks oxygen. In every case make sure that his line is tended by another man.

The hazard of electrical shock has increased aboard ship with the introduction of much new electronic equipment. The Officer of the Deck will be mainly concerned with men requesting permission to work aloft, but if any of the electronic gear on the bridge is under repair he should check to see that it has been de-energized. Safety interlocks have been known to fail. Upon receiving a request from men who have work to do aloft, the Officer of the Deck should first call the appropriate officers or petty officers and make sure that all power is turned off aloft and that radar antennas and gun directors will not be rotated. This involves taking positive action not only to cut off power but to insure, by the use of signs, locks, or sentries, that someone coming along does not close the switch. Safety belts should, of course, be used by men who must work in the rigging, and their tools should be secured to their persons. Chapter 67, *Bureau of Ships Manual,* lists detailed precautions to be taken by men who work on electronic equipment. An all-too-common type of electric shock casualty is caused by ungrounded power hand tools. This is not normally within the purview of the Officer of the Deck, but in port a check of welding machines and power tools used topside can be made by the Junior Officer of the Watch. Most power tools also require the use of goggles by the operator. Goggles are important safety devices often neglected by careless men.

Fueling and provisioning at sea, gunnery practices,

heavy weather, and other special events or circumstances all call for specific precautions to safeguard personnel. The ship's organization book is usually the best source of information on these matters.

RELATIONS WITH THE ENGINEERS

"The engineering officer of the watch shall insure that all orders received from the officer of the deck are promptly and properly executed."—*U.S. Navy Regulations, 1948* (Art. 1027).

A fully qualified Officer of the Deck should have some knowledge of his ship's engineering plant. In a steam driven ship he should know in detail the relationship between boilers and maximum speed and the time required to light off and cut in additional boilers. He should appreciate the special problems that the engineer department must meet in frequent and radical changes in speed, particularly in regard to superheat, and in changing the direction of rotation of the propellers. There are many other engineering problems that sometimes involve the Officer of the Deck, such as fuel, water, and electrical power consumption, the need for blowing tubes, and the operation of the ship's boats. In order to make reasonable decisions and to exercise correct judgment and foresight, the Officer of the Deck should have a considerable basic knowledge, not only of the plant itself, but of the organization of the engineer department as well. When on watch he must not act as a deck or communication division officer; his primary interest is the welfare and efficiency of the whole ship.

By far the most important point for the Officer of the Deck to remember concerning engineer personnel is to *keep them informed* well ahead of time. Main propulsion machinery is not automatic; men have to operate it, and these men must know, in general, what is planned and what is going on topside. An efficient Officer of the Deck keeps the engineers in mind at all times and sees that any messages or other directives that involve movement of the ship are routed below to the Engineer Officer of the Watch and to the Engineer Officer. Radical changes of speed are particularly important matters to engineering personnel.

INSPECTIONS

"The officer of the deck shall require frequent inspections to be made to insure the security of the ship, including watertight integrity, degree of closure, condition of the armament, condition of ground tackle or mooring lines in use, good order and discipline of the crew and all other matters which may effect the safety or operations of the ship. Such of the above inspections as are not made and reported to him by another regularly established watch shall be made by members of his watch."—*U.S. Navy Regulations, 1948* (Art. 1013).

No matter how busy or even hectic a watch may be, the Officer of the Deck must remember that his responsibilities include the whole ship. The security of the ship depends on frequent inspections to insure that no fire hazards exist and that watertight fittings required to be closed are actually dogged down. At the same time discipline and order must be maintained among the crew. Ninety-nine times out of a hundred the men will maintain order themselves, but it has happened, and will happen again, that a few black sheep will get into trouble. A common example is the consumption of liquor that has been smuggled aboard, accompanied by gambling, fighting, etc. A fatal stabbing on an LSD a few years after the war, and the more recent hold-up of a large dice game aboard a carrier, are examples of what can happen. A properly organized ship provides for necessary inspections of all parts of the ship at irregular intervals.

Inspections normally include a watertight integrity security patrol made at regular intervals by damage control personnel. Tanks and voids are sounded during these patrols. Other inspections may be made to safeguard classified matter or to guard against damage to boats secured aft or riding at a boom. In large ships a check-off list of all inspections and patrols is a useful device that can be maintained by the boatswain's mate or the quartermaster of the watch.

THE MASTER-AT-ARMS

"In ships . . . there shall be assigned under the executive officer a chief master-at-arms, and such other masters-at-arms, as may be required as his assistants, for the maintenance of good order and discipline."—*U.S. Navy Regulations, 1948* (Art. 0806).

The chief master-at-arms, or in his absence, the duty master-at-arms, is a valuable assistant to the Officer of the Deck. He should be notified when changes in the day's routine are under consideration. He should also be used in making inspections. Above all, he is a major factor in maintaining order throughout the ship. From conducting the Commanding Officer to the movies at night, to handling a noisy and obstreperous drunk returning from liberty, the master-at-arms is an invaluable aid to the Officer of the Deck. See the ship's organization book for detailed duties of the master-at-arms.

EIGHT O'CLOCK REPORTS

Eight o'clock reports are an important part of the ship's routine. They serve two functions: to insure that the necessary security and damage control inspections and checks have been made, and to furnish the Executive Officer with the information he needs to make his report on the condition of the ship at 2000 to the Commanding Officer. (In accordance with time-honored custom of the service, the reports made to the Executive Officer or Command Duty Officer by the heads of departments at 2000 are known as the *eight o'clock* reports, not the *twenty hundred reports.*)

CUSTODY OF KEYS

A matter of minor importance that can prove difficult to the Officer of the Deck, is the custody of ship's keys. Heads of departments are normally responsible for the keys to locked spaces under their cognizance, except that the keys to magazines are kept by the Commanding Officer and those to lockers containing alcohol and drugs are usually in the custody of the Executive Officer or Medical Officer. Narcotics are kept in a safe with an officer custodian having the combination. If keys are kept in their specified places and are not carried on the person of some petty officer, then all those with proper authorization can obtain ready entry to locked spaces. More important, in the event of an emergency such as fire, access can readily be obtained to locked compartments or storerooms. The Officer of the Deck should discourage the men from carrying keys on their belts or, worse, going ashore with them. It is only human nature to want to feel important, and this is usually the motive that impels a man to collect a large group of keys. An indication of this bad practice is often the request, as mentioned in Chapter I, of asking the Officer of the Deck to pass the word for someone with certain keys.

DAMAGE CONTROL SETTINGS

The qualified Officer of the Deck requires a reasonably thorough knowledge of the damage control organization of his ship. He must know how certain closures are made as a matter of routine, and must know the system in force for maintaining watertight security. The usual practice in small ships includes a watertight closure log, kept by the quartermaster of the watch, in which are recorded the openings permitted, upon request, by the Officer of the Deck. Both time of opening and time of closure are logged. At general quarters the log is maintained in Damage Control Central. In large ships Damage Control Central is manned at all times when underway and the watertight log is maintained there.

While this business of opening and closing doors and hatches may appear rather dull and routine, it is a matter of great importance to the safety of the ship and the lives of the crew. A ship can go along for years and never suffer for having neglected her watertight integrity, but a sudden grounding or collision may result in disaster if the ship lacks watertight integrity. Even half a ship will stay afloat and permit the rescue of many men if the watertight integrity has been maintained. The Officer of the Deck must always be cognizant of the need for combatting carelessness and for making sure that his ship is properly secured.

RELATIONS WITH AN EMBARKED STAFF

The Officer of the Deck of a flagship has the additional responsibilities of keeping the embarked staff informed, of handling additional boats and vehicles, and, of course, of rendering additional honors.

The staff duty officer is normally the person who should receive special reports. In general, the incidents, events, and sightings normally reported to the Commanding Officer should also be reported to the staff duty officer. He bears about the same relation to his Admiral as an Officer of the Deck does to the Commanding Officer.

Staff officers exercise care to preserve the unity of command of the flagship and do not give orders directly to the Officer of the Deck. Routine requests may be made to officers of the flagship, but in matters of any importance the chief of staff usually deals with the Commanding Officer of the flagship. An Officer of the Deck will not be inconvenienced by an embarked staff so long as he remembers to consider their needs, and *above all,* to keep them informed.

MATERIAL CASUALTIES

The Officer of the Deck must insure that all machinery and electronic gear is operable within, of course, the limits of his capabilities. This means that foresight is necessary in testing equipment that may be used in the immediate future. Power or steam to winches or windlasses, radars started and tested, radios energized and tuned—all these are typical examples. In addition, the Officer of the Deck should follow up any material casualties that occur so that he may be certain that the cognizant officer is notified immediately. An electronic failure, for example, should be reported personally to the Electronics Officer as well as to the Captain and Admiral (if embarked), and information should be obtained concerning estimated length of repair time. This will permit you, as Officer of the Deck, to give the Captain and the staff duty officer a sensible answer when they inquire about the casualty.

RATIONS

"Each meal served in the general mess shall be sampled by an officer detailed by the commanding officer for that purpose. Should this officer find the quality or quantity of food unsatisfactory, or should any member of the mess object to the quality or quantity of the food, the commanding officer shall be immediately notified and he shall take appropriate action."—*U.S. Navy Regulations, 1948* (Art. 1982).

It is normal procedure for the Officer of the Deck to be supplied with a sample ration in compliance with the directive quoted above. He should make certain that the portion sent up is truly a representative one and not carefully selected from the food being served the crew. A better procedure, when conditions permit, is to send the Junior Officer of the Watch below to draw a ration from the food line. The latter officer can then note other items, such as the manner in which the food is served, as well as the cleanliness of the food handlers.

In addition to the three regularly scheduled meals it is a naval custom of long standing to serve some sort of a night ration to those having the midwatch. A snack during the night helps the men to wake up fully and is conducive to a better watch through the increased contentment and efficiency of the men. In cold weather, especially, a night ration is almost a necessity, since the human body needs much more fuel when working in low temperatures.

The Officer of the Deck, in appreciating the useful purpose of a night ration, should determine whether or not the ration is being distributed fairly and equitably. Cooks and commissary personnel put in a long, hard day and are not usually enthusiastic on the subject of extra food at night. A moderate amount of supervision is often required to insure that the food is ready and is distributed.

OBSERVERS

Officers and men who come aboard to observe gunnery practices and other exercises are often a source of concern for the Officer of the Deck. He sometimes has to order a Jacob's ladder slung over the side and see that the party is fed and, at times, berthed. The chief master-at-arms normally takes care of the men with the Executive Officer, the First Lieutenant, or the wardroom mess caterer looking after the officers. It is the Officer of the Deck's responsibility to see that these domestic duties are performed, and that a maximum amount of hospitality and consideration is shown the visitors. Foresight must be exercised, particularly in rounding up all the party preparatory to departure, to avoid keeping boats, and sometimes senior officers, waiting.

CLASSIFIED PUBLICATIONS ON THE BRIDGE

It is usually necessary to maintain on the bridge (in the pilothouse) an extensive collection of classified material. Signal books and tactical publications are often registered and must be in someone's custody at all times. Upon getting underway it is customary for the ship's custodian to bring the classified publications up to the bridge and to obtain the signature of the Officer of the Deck or Junior Officer of the Watch then on duty. Whoever signs must in turn obtain the signature of his successor as the watch is relieved. It is best for the Junior Officer of the Watch to assume this recurrent duty and to keep custody of the bridge publications. He should sight each publication before signing the list.

BINOCULARS AND STADIMETERS

Radar has tended to de-emphasize the care and skilful use of binoculars on the bridge. This tendency is recognized by experienced officers as an unfortunate one. There are frequent occasions when the human eye has more range and discrimination than radar. Conditions of electronic silence may, in future wartime operations, again require the old fashioned ability to see well at night.

The Officer of the Deck should know how to adjust, clean, and use a pair of binoculars. He should know his own focus and inter-pupillary setting. He should also be capable of instructing his lookouts and other personnel in the care and use of the glasses. Careless handling, especially dropping, can soon render a pair of glasses unfit for use until repairs are made by a tender or shipyard. The men should be taught to use the neck strap and to keep the glasses in a case when not actually in use. Nothing is more lubberly, unseamanlike, and just plain wasteful of public funds than leaving binoculars adrift. The top of a chart table may seem like safe stowage until the ship takes a roll and you are faced with the embarrassment of having to lean over and pick up a pair of useless glasses. There are only two places on the bridge for binoculars: on a strap around the user's neck, or stowed in a case or in a rack. Remember that binoculars are cleaned only with lens paper; cloth will scratch the lenses.

Many of the remarks made above concerning binoculars are applicable to stadimeters. Their use, adjustment, and care are still matters of importance to an Officer of the Deck. Do not depend on your quartermaster to line up the stadimeter you are using. Do it yourself, and most important of all, check it each time you use it. Keep it stowed in its box or in clips attached to the overhead bulkhead.

PETTY OFFICERS AS OFFICERS OF THE DECK

On small ships it is often necessary to use chief petty officers or petty officers as Officers of the Deck. There should be no confusion as to the official status of these petty officers so assigned; they are Officers of the Deck, subject only in the performance of duty to the orders of the Commanding Officer, Executive Officer, and Command Duty Officer. The assignment of petty officers as Officers of the Deck should be made in writing in the ship's organization book, the senior watch officer's watch list, or in the Plan of the Day.

Chapter IV

THE DECK LOG

"The deck log shall be a complete daily record, by watches, in which shall be described every circumstance and occurrence of importance or interest which concerns the crew and the operation and safety of the ship, or which may be of historical value. . . . *U. S. Navy Regulations, 1948* (Art. 1037).

GENERAL

The deck log is the only official chronological record of the ship's history during her commission. It presents a complete, accurate narrative of noteworthy incidents in the life of the ship and events affecting her officers, passengers and crew. All significant items, whether pertaining to the ship's personnel, material, operations, or state of readiness, are entered in the deck log. It thus becomes at once the true historical account of the ship's activities and an accurate source of factual and legal data. It also provides essential aerological and hydrographic data in plain terms for the command and in more detailed synoptic code for climatological records. Watch officers responsible for the preparation of the log must understand and appreciate the importance of their undertaking. They must insure that all entries are complete, accurate, clear, concise, and expressed in standard naval phraseology. Entries must connote a true and understandable historical and legal record of the ship.

There are two parts of the deck log to be written for each watch. The first consists of tabular data which are entered in various columns. These data include the state of the weather and synoptic weather reports as well as certain logistic data and ship's position reports. Although these entries generally are made by the quartermaster of the watch, the Officer of the Deck is responsible for the accuracy of all entries. He must frequently review the weather observation entries to determine that they are consistent with actual changes in the weather. Unless this is done, the weather entries may remain unchanged regardless of how much the weather itself may have changed. Constant vigilance, indoctrination, and care on the part of observing personnel are required to insure that the weather elements are accurately evaluated and correctly entered in the log. The Manual of Synoptic Weather Observations for Ship's Deck Log (OPNAVINST 3140.37) contains detailed information and guidance in taking and recording weather observations at sea and should be consulted.

The second part of the deck log consists of the remarks of the Officer of the Deck concerning the miscellaneous events that took place during his watch. In order to properly evaluate and enter the required remarks into the deck log, the Officer of the Deck and his assistants must be familiar with, and understand, the regulations and requirements for such entries. The Instructions for Keeping Ship's Deck Log (NAVPERS-15876) is found in the Deck Log Book and includes extracts from the United States Navy Regulations and the Naval Supplement to the Manual for Courts Martial United States, 1951, relative to the Ship's Deck Log. Sample entries are also included.

The quartermaster's notebook, in a large part, forms the basis for the Officer of the Deck's remarks. The Officer of the Deck should supervise its keeping, requiring that all pertinent information and data relative to each event or occurrence throughout the watch, including exact times, be entered accurately and chronologically as they occur. It is difficult, if not impossible, to write a good log without a well-written quartermaster's notebook.

The quartermaster's notebook should be kept in great detail. Every event should be entered in full at the time it occurs. In writing his remarks, the Officer of the Deck may or may not include details found in the quartermaster's notebook, depending upon the importance of the event or the outcome of a series of events. For example, the quartermaster's notebook should include each change of course—true, per gyro compass (pgc), and per standard compass (psc)—and speed. The Officer of the Deck's remarks for entering or leaving port or conducting an exercise may summarize this as "steering various courses at various speeds," if the exercise was accomplished without incident. Each aid to navigation sighted (including buoys) and the times when they are passed abeam and lost from sight (for the major ones), should be entered in the quartermaster's notebook. When these aids to navigation are very numerous, the Officer of the Deck need only list a few of the more prominent ones. Every contact, whether visual, radar, or sonar, must be logged by the quartermaster. When visual and radar contacts prove false, their inclusion in the deck log would merely clutter up the log and obscure important remarks. However, in case of a grounding, collision, or other damage, the Officer of the Deck should make his account in great detail. In general, the entries in the Officer of the Deck's remarks section should not duplicate any data listed in tabular form.

The writing of the rough deck log should be done while the events are still fresh in your memory. Never leave the bridge or deck until your log is written.

"The officer of the deck shall insure that the rough deck log for his watch is complete, accurate, and clear; and he shall sign it on being relieved."—*U. S. Navy Regulations, 1948* (Art. 1022).

The entries in the deck log for any one day should give a complete account of the events of that day, from 0000 until 2400, without the necessity of referring back to the logs of previous days. Therefore, the remarks for the mid-watch should start off with a concise yet complete summation of the situation existing at midnight. This should include the location and status of the ship, command relations, other ships and units present, and, when appropriate, the weather conditions. Succeeding watches need only have events listed as they occur.

"No erasures shall be made in the deck log, quartermaster's notebook, magnetic compass record book, engineering log, or engineer's bell book. When a correction is deemed necessary, a single line shall be drawn through the original entry so that the entry remains legible. The correct entry shall then be inserted in such manner as to insure clarity and legibility. Corrections, additions, or changes shall be made only by the person required to sign the record for the watch, and shall be initialed by him on the margin of the page.

"Should the commanding officer direct a change or addition to one of the foregoing records, the person concerned shall comply, unless he believes the proposed change or addition to be incorrect; in which event the commanding officer shall enter such remarks on the record over his signature as he deems appropriate.

"No change shall be made on a log after it has been signed by the commanding officer, without his permission or direction."—*U. S. Navy Regulations, 1948* (Art. 1036).

The rough deck log, along with the quartermaster's notebook, magnetic compass record book, the rough engineering log, and the engineer's bell book, is at times used as evidence before courts and other legal bodies. It is therefore important that, under circumstances that might conceivably lead to legal action, the remarks be particularly complete and accurate. Under such circumstances, it is advisable that they first be written in rough draft form, then checked for completeness and accuracy by all concerned, and submitted to the Navigator and Captain for comment prior to entry in the log. Erasures in either the deck log, magnetic compass record book or the quartermaster's notebook, would open to question their validity as evidence.

The log is often consulted years later in regard to claims for pensions by persons who served in the Armed Forces and those who claim injury while in the Service. A complete entry, therefore, must be made in the log of each and every injury, accident or casualty, including accidents which could lead to later disclosure of injuries to the officers, crew, or passengers on board. This is necessary both to protect the government from false claims and to furnish a record for honest claimants.

The Navigator has charge of the preparation of the deck log. By Regulations he is required to examine the log book to see that it is prepared in accordance with instructions, and to call the attention of watch officers to any inaccuracies or omissions in their entries. The Navigator is responsible to the Commanding Officer that the entries in the log are in proper form; but the Officer of the Deck is responsible for the entries during his watch.

It is the responsibility of each watch officer to promptly verify and sign the smooth remarks sheet of his watch upon completion of its preparation. Prior to going on leave or being detached from the ship each deck watch officer must insure that the smooth remarks have been prepared, verified and signed for any watch he may have stood.

As a matter of custom and tradition the first watch of the year is written in verse.

SAMPLE ENTRIES

The following sample entries are offered as guidance in the writing of the remarks for a watch. Such a list of samples, of course, cannot be all inclusive, nor can they be considered the only acceptable entries. Any entry that is complete, accurate, clear, and in standard naval phraseology will be acceptable.

ABBREVIATIONS, POLICY WITH REGARD TO

In general, abbreviations in the deck log shall be limited to those commonly recognized and those generally accepted throughout the Naval service. Obscure or communication type abbreviations shall not be used. The following is a partial listing of the more commonly used abbreviations:

AWOL	Absence over leave/liberty or absence without leave
c/c	Changed course
c/s	Changed speed
CPA	Closest point of approach
OCE	Officer conducting the exercise
OOD	Officer of the Deck
OTC	Officer in Tactical Command
SOP	Senior Officer Present
SOPA	Senior Officer Present Afloat
UCMJ	Uniform Code of Military Justice, 1948

Command and Bureau Abbreviations: DesDiv21, ComDesDiv21, VC 23, BuPers, etc.

State Abbreviations: Mass.—Massachusetts, etc.

AIR OPERATIONS

Carrier

1000 Flight Quarters.

1005—Commenced launching aircraft for (carrier qualification) (refresher operations) (group tactics), etc. Base Course ———.

1025 Completed launching aircraft, having launched 40 aircraft.

1030 Commenced recovering aircraft. Base Course ________.

1035 Commenced maneuvering, on various courses (and speeds) while recovering (launching) aircraft (while conducting task group (force) flight operations).

1055 Completed recovering aircraft, having recovered 40 aircraft.

1143 F9F BuNo. 10678 of VF 75, pilot CDR John P. JONES, USN, 553262, crashed into sea off the port bow at Latitude 36° 50′ N, Longitude 74° 31′ W, and sank in 500 fathoms of water.

1144 (U.S.S.) HARLAN R. DICKSON (DD 708) and helicopter commenced search for pilot (if applicable).

1146 Pilot recovered by helicopter and delivered (on board) to (U.S.S.) MIDWAY (CVA 41), injuries to pilot: (description).

1200 Search concluded. Results negative. Pilot CDR John P. JONES, USN, 553262, presumed dead, (if applicable).

1215 Secured from Flight Quarters.

1300 F2H BuNo. 69696 of VC 5, pilot, ENS John P. JONES, USN, 532961, crashed into barriers numbers 2, 4, and 6 and turned over. Pilot sustained mild abrasion to left forearm and both legs. Damage to aircraft: major (minor) (strike).

1315 CDR A. B. SEA, USN, Commanding VF 25, departed with 17 aircraft for Elizabeth City, N.J., TAD completed.

1330 CDR X. Y. ZEE, USN, Commanding VF 26, landed aboard with 18 aircraft from NAS, Norfolk, Va., for TAD.

Note: During flight operations and other maneuvering log the Base Course and speed. Minor changes may be covered by: "Maneuvering on various courses . . . etc." All changes, however, must be entered in the quartermaster's notebook.

Entries Applicable to Ships Carrying Helicopters

1435 Flight Quarters. 1455 Launched helicopter. Pilot: LTJG L. T. BOYD, USNR-R. Passenger: BORE, J. T., BMC. 1505 Recovered helicopter on main deck aft. 1510 Secured from flight quarters.

Loading Aircraft

0800 Commenced hoisting aircraft of VF 21 (CVG7) aboard. 1000 Completed hoisting 25 aircraft of VF 21 aboard.

AMMUNITION

1400 Commenced loading (transferring) ammunition.
1600 Completed loading (transferring) ammunition, having received (from NAD, Mare Island, Calif.) transferred to (U.S.S.) PRAIRIE (AD 15) 400 rounds 5″/38 cal. illum. projectiles, 250 5″/38 cal. smokeless and 250 5″/38 cal. flashless charges.

Note: For entries regarding expenditure of ammunition, see Exercises.

DAMAGE

1155 (U.S.S) BOOTH (DE 170) in coming alongside to port, carried away 39 feet of the ship's port lifeline forward, with stanchions, and indented the ship's side to a depth of 4″ over a space 10 feet long and 4 feet high in the vicinity of frames 46-51. No personnel casualties.
1401 Starboard lifeboat carried away by heavy sea. Boat and all equipment lost. No personnel casualties.

DRILLS AND EXERCISES

1100 Exercised at General Drills.

Abandon Ship

1105 Held abandon ship drill, provide.
1115 Secured from abandon ship drill.

ABC Attack

1440 Set material condition ______ and ABC condition ______. 1450 Set ABC condition ______. 1500 (simulated) atomic (underwater) (air) burst, bearing ______ distance ______ yards. Maneuvering on various courses at various speeds to avoid base surge and fall out. 1530 Rejoined formation and took station ______ in formation ______. Axis, course, speed, etc.

Collision

1350 Held collision drill. 1354 Material condition ______ set. 1410 Secured from collision drill. Set material condition ______.

Fire

1100 Held fire drill. 1110 Secured from fire drill.

Fire and Rescue

1300 Called away the fire and rescue party.

1305 Fire and rescue party embarked in starboard boat and clear of ship.

1330 Fire and rescue party returned aboard.

Gunnery

1245 Went to General Quarters. Set material condition ______. 1300 Commenced ______ exercise. 1304 Commenced firing to starboard (port). 1308 Ceased fire. 1320 Set material condition ______. 1325 Secured from General Quarters. Ammunition expended: 24 rounds 6″/47 cal. dye loaded, etc.

FORMATION

0700 Maneuvering to take station ______ in formation ______, axis ______, course ______, speed ______ knots. Guide is (U.S.S.) ROCHESTER (CA 124) in station ______. 0800 Rotated formation axis to ______. 0900 Formation changed from 49 to 52. New course and axis ______, speed ______ knots. Formation Guide is (U.S.S.) COLUMBUS (CA 74) in station ______.

Officer in Tactical Command (OTC)

0900 ComCarDiv 4, embarked in the (U.S.S.) MIDWAY (CVA 41), assumed OTC.

1000 Commanding Officer, (U.S.S.) FRANKLIN D. ROOSEVELT (CVA 42) was designated OTC.

Note: Log all shifts of tactical command. When the OTC is the Commanding Officer of your vessel, use the following terminology: "OTC is Commanding Officer, (U.S.S.) FRANKLIN D. ROOSEVELT (CVA 42)." In every case, use command title of OTC, not his name and rank: for example, ComCarDiv 2. State in which vessel the OTC is embarked.

Rendezvous

0800 (U.S.S.) JAMES C. OWENS (DD 776) made rendezvous with this vessel (the formation) and took designated station (took station in the screen) (took plane guard station).

2200 Joined rendezvous with TG 19.9 and took designated station number ______ in formation 4R, with guide in (U.S.S.) SALEM (CA 139) bearing 095, distance 2400 yards, formation course ______, formation speed ______ knots, axis ______. OTC is ComCarDiv 4 in (U.S.S.) MIDWAY (CVA 41).

Tactical Exercises

1000 Commenced division tactical exercises. Steering various courses at various speeds (in Area HOW) (conforming to maneuvers signalled by ComDesRon 12) (on signals from ComDesRon 12).

Zigzagging/Sinuating

1300 Commenced zigzagging in accordance with Plan #______ base course ______. 1350 Ceased zigzagging and set course ______.

1400 Commenced steering sinuous course, Cam #1, base course ______. 1600 Ceased steering sinuous course and set course ______.

FUELING

In port

1000 Commenced fueling from (U.S.S.) SALAMONIE (AO 26) (Naval Fuel Depot, Cheatham Annex) draft forward ______, aft ______. 1200 Fueling completed, draft forward ______, aft ______.

At sea

1000 Formed fueling disposition ______.

1100 Left station and maneuvered to standby station astern of (U.S.S.) CALOOSAHATCHEE (AO 98). 1120 (U.S.S.) HARLAN R. DICKSON (DD 708) cast off from CALOOSAHATCHEE and maneuvered clear. Commenced approach to port side of oiler, Captain (conning) (at the conn). 1125 Received first fuel hose, 1127 Commenced receiving fuel.

1146 Fueling completed. 1157 All lines and hoses clear. Maneuvered to regain station.

HONORS, CEREMONIES, OFFICIAL VISITS

Visits

1430 Their Hellenic Majestics, the King and Queen of Greece, made an official call on VADM D. G. FARRAGUT, USN, ComSixthFlt, with their official parties. Rendered honors and fired a salute of 21 guns. 1530 The Royal Party departed. Rendered honors and fired a salute of 21 guns.

Calls

1000 The Commanding Officer left the ship to call officially on ComCruDiv 4.

1601 RADM G. DEWEY, USN, ComCruDiv 4, came on board to return the official call of the Commanding Officer.

Flags, Personal

1200 RADM J. BARRY, USN, ComCruDiv 2, broke his flag in this vessel.

1300 The Honorable ____________________, Secretary of the Navy, came on board; broke the flag of the Secretary of the Navy. 1500 The Secretary of the Navy departed; hauled down the flag of the Secretary of the Navy.

1530 ComCruDesPac shifted his flag from (U.S.S.) PRAIRIE (AD 15) to (U.S.S.) DIXIE (AD 14).

INSPECTIONS

Administrative, Personnel, Readiness

0930 RADM W. BAINBRIDGE, USN, ComTraComdLant, accompanied by members of his staff and inspecting party from (U.S.S.) WISCONSIN (BB 64), came on board and commenced surprise (administrative, personnel, readiness) inspection. Broke flag of ComTraComdLant.

1100 ComTraComdLant, members of his staff, and inspecting party left the ship. 1110 ComTraComdLant broke his flag in (U.S.S.) WISCONSIN (BB 64).

Lower Deck

1315 Commenced captain's inspection of lower decks, holds, and storerooms. 1400 Secured from inspection.

Magazines

1000 Made daily inspection of magazines and smokeless powder samples; conditions normal. 1000 Made weekly test of magazine sprinkling and flooding system; conditions satisfactory. 1000 Completed semiannual surveillance tests of all (five inch) (main battery) smokeless (flashless) powder samples. Conditions satisfactory.

Note: Where test is of a continuing nature on a large number of lots, and only part have been completed, list lot numbers of samples tested.

Personnel

0900 Mustered the crew at quarters for Captain's inspection (of personnel and upper decks).

1010 Secured from inspection.

MIDWATCH ENTRIES

Underway

00-04 Steaming in company with Task Group 58.1, composed of CarDiv 1, CruDiv 3, and DesRon 5 plus (U.S.S.) MADISON (DD 425) and (U.S.S.) CHARLES E. BRANNON (DE 446), enroute from Pearl Harbor, T.H. to Guam, M.I. (Operating at sea off the coast of California) in accordance with CTG 58.1 serial 061. This ship in station ______ in bent line screen ______. Formation course ______, speed ______ knots. Formation axis ______. SOPA is CTG 58.1 in (U.S.S.) ROCHESTER (CA 124), OTC is ComCruDiv 3 in (U.S.S.) SALEM (CA 139). ROCHESTER is guide, bearing ______, distance ______ yards. Conditions of readiness two and material condition ______ set. Ship darkened (except for running lights).

Note: On succeeding watches the first entry is "Anchored as before," "Steaming as before," "Underway as before," "Moored as before," whichever is applicable.

In port

00-04 Moored starboard side to (U.S.S.) HARLAN R. DICKSON (DD 708) with standard mooring lines in a nest of three destroyers. (U.S.S.) KNAPP (DD 653) moored outboard of HARLAN R. DICKSON to starboard. HARLAN R. DICKSON moored fore and aft to buoys B-5 and B-6, San Diego, Calif. Ships present: ______. SOPA ______.

00-04 Anchored in Berth B-4, U. S. Naval Operating Base, Trinidad, BWI, in 11 fathoms of water, mud bottom, with 60 fathoms of chain to the starboard anchor on the following anchorage bearings: South Point Light 060, etc. Ship in condition of readiness three, material condition ______ set, and darkened except for anchor lights. Engineering department on 30 minutes notice for getting underway. Heavy weather plan in effect. Anchor detail standing by. Wind 45 knots from 070. Weather reports indicate possibility of winds up to 60 knots before 0400. Ships present: etc. SOPA ______.

00-04 Moored starboard side to Pier 3, Berth 35, U. S. Naval Operating Base, Norfolk, Va. with standard mooring lines doubled. Receiving miscellaneous services from the pier. Ships present include ______. SOPA is ______.

00-04 Resting on keel blocks in Drydock Number Three, U. S. Naval Shipyard, Bremerton, Washington, receiving miscellaneous services from the dock. SOPA is ______. Ships present include ______.

NAVIGATIONAL ENTRIES

Anchoring

1600 Anchored in Area South HOW, Berth 44, Hampton Roads, Virginia, in 4 fathoms of water, mud bottom, with 30 fathoms of chain to the port anchor on the following bearings: Fort Wool 040, Middle Ground Light 217, Sewall Point 072. Ships present: ______. SOPA is ComBatDiv 1 in (U.S.S.) MISSOURI (BB 63).

Note: For ships present entries see Ships Present.

Contacts

1405 Sighted merchant vessel bearing 280 distance about 6 miles on approximately parallel course.

1430 Identified merchant vessel as S.S. SEAKAY U. S. registry, routed independently from Aruba, NWI, to

New York, N.Y. 1441 Passed S.S. SEAKAY abeam to port, distance about 2 miles.

1621 Obtained unidentified radar contact bearing 090 distance 28,800 yds. (14 miles). 1629 Unidentified contact tracked and determined to be on course 180, speed 15 knots. CPA 042, distance 4.2 miles. 1636 Contact identified as (U.S.S.) KNAPP (DD 653) by (U.S.S.) BASILONE (DDE 824).

1715 Obtained sonar contact bearing 172 range 2,500 yds. 1717 Contact evaluated as possible submarine. Commenced attack (tracking) (investigating). 1720 Lost contact. 1721 Contact regained bearing 020, range ______. Oil slick sighted on that bearing and range. Commenced re-attack. 1724 Sonar reported hearing breaking up noises. 1725 Contact lost. Steering various courses at ______ knots to regain station in formation. 1811 Regained station.

Course

1005 With Navassa Island Light abeam to port, distance 12 miles, changed course to 195.

1204 With New York Harbor swept channel buoy "XA" abeam to port (close aboard) (distance 500 yds) took departure for Boston, Mass. and set course 085, speed ______ knots.

1600 Completed division tactical exercises and set course 180, speed ______ knots. In column formation, OTC in (U.S.S.) NEW JERSEY (BB 62). Order of ships: NEW JERSEY (Guide), (U.S.S.) WILKES-BARRE (CL 103) (U.S.S.) MADISON (DD 425). Distance 1000 yds.

Note:

(1) Unless otherwise noted, bearings and courses are understood to read "degrees true."

(2) Where doubt may exist as to the course when passing an object abeam, as when maneuvering on various courses, log bearing when abeam.

(3) Course is "set" upon taking departure and upon completion of maneuvers.

Drydocking

1420 Tug SEAGOOSE came alongside to port, Pilot A. B. SEA came on board. 1426 YTM 68 came alongside port bow, YTM 63 came alongside port quarter. 1431 First line to dock starboard bow. 1435 First line to dock port bow. 1440 Bow passed over sill of dock. 1450 Caisson in place. 1455 Commenced pumping water out of drydock. 1540 Resting on keel blocks. 1545 Pilot left the ship. 1550 Commenced receiving electrical power, fresh and flushing water from dock. 1630 Inspection completed all hull openings.

Undocking

0850 Inspection completed of all hull openings. 0900 Flooding commenced in drydock. 0918 All services disconnected from ship. 0920 Ship clear of keel blocks. 0925 Inspection completed of all spaces for watertight integrity. 0930 Handling lines secure on ship. 0935 Pilot A. B. SEA came on board. 0950 Commenced moving ship clear of dock. 0958 Stern passed over sill. 1005 YTM 68 alongside port quarter. 1008 YTM 63 came alongside port bow. 1009 Bow passed over sill.

Harbor (entering)

0551 Passed Ambrose Lightship abeam to port, distance ________. 0554 Stationed special sea detail. OOD (conning) (at the conn), Captain and Navigator on the bridge. 0600 Entered inland waters. Draft: forward ________, aft ________. 0619 Changed course to ________, speed ________ knots. 0636 Commenced steering various courses at various speeds conforming to Gedney channel. 0650 Passed lighted buoy No. 12 abeam to starboard. 0701 Stopped all engines.

0705 U. S. Navy Tug No. 216 came alongside port quarter. Pilot W. Y. ZEE came aboard and took the

conn. 0706 Maneuvering to go alongside pier.
0715 Moored port side to berth 3A, U. S. Naval Ammunition Depot, Earle, N.J., with standard mooring lines. Ships present: ______. SOPA is ComDesDiv 22 in (U.S.S.) LAFFEY (DD 724). 0720 Pilot left the ship.

Note: Salient points of the ship's navigation should be logged for clarifying the ship's position. Names of tugs, stating whether Navy or commercial, and names of pilots should always be logged, giving time of arrival and time of departure. All course and speed changes, buoys, and times of entering and leaving specific channels must be entered in quartermaster's notebook.

Mooring

1006 Moored port side to Standard Oil Dock, Berth 76, Los Angeles Inner Harbor, Calif., with standard mooring lines. 1015 Commenced receiving miscellaneous services from the pier.

Sighting Aids to Navigation

0102 Sighted Cape Henry Light bearing 225 distance about 20 miles. 0157 Passed Cape Henry Light abeam to starboard, distance 7.3 miles. 0300 Cape Henry Light passed from view bearing 315, distance about 20 miles.

Speed

1700 Increased speed to ______ knots. 1710 c/s to ______ knots. 1713 Decreased speed to ______ knots to prevent damage to small boats alongside pier 7.

Tide

0733 Commenced swinging to flood tide, stern to port. 1046 Completed swinging to flood tide, heading 347.

Time Zone Change

0001 Set clocks ahead one hour to conform with +3 Zone Time.

Underway (getting)

0600 Commenced preparations for getting underway. Set material condition ______. 0730 Stationed the special sea detail. 0750 Completed all preparations for getting underway. Draft: forward ______, aft______. 0800 Underway for Norfolk, Va. (for sea) as a unit of Task Group 73.4 in compliance with ComCarDiv 4 serial 063 (CTG 63.4 OpOrder 3-53). Maneuvering to clear the anchorage. Captain (conning) (at the conn), Navigator on the bridge. 0810 Steering various courses at various speeds standing out of Boston Harbor. 0830 Officer of the Deck (OOD) was given the conn. Set condition of readiness three, anchor detail on deck. (Secured special sea detail, set the regular steaming watch). 0845 Entered international waters.

Weather

1130 Visibility decreased to one mile due to fog (heavy rain). Commenced sounding fog signals and stationed (extra lookouts) (lookouts in the eyes of the ship).

1212 Visibility increased to five miles. Ceased sounding fog signals.

Note: The entry for commencing and ceasing to sound fog signals must always be entered. Any major change in visibility should also be entered.

OFFICERS

Detachment

1400 Pursuant to BuPers msg 011630Z May, LT Robert R. JONES, USN, 426106, was detached from this ship with orders to report to Com 14 for duty (transportation).

Leave

1100 ComDesRon 3 hauled down his pennant and departed on 4 days leave.

1100 Captain departed on six days leave.

2212 Captain returned from six days leave.

Note: Flag officers and unit commanders embarked and commanding officers are the only personnel who must be logged out and in on leave.

Reporting

1400 In accordance with BuPers msg 111620Z May, LT. R. R. JONES, USNR, 426106, reported on board for duty (as Engineer Officer), (transportation to Pearl Harbor, T.H.) (temporary duty in connection with ______).

Temporary Duty

1400 Pursuant to CincPacFlt serial 4217 of 21 May 1953, ENS W. P. JONES, USN, 123456, left the ship for temporary duty with Com 14.

1700 ENS W. P. JONES, USN, 123456, having completed temporary duty with Com 14, returned on board and resumed his regular duties.

PASSENGERS

1000 Mr. Albert M. JONES (Civilian Technician) embarked for transportation to Pearl Harbor, T. H. Authority: CNO msg 141120Z, May.

Note: All passengers should be logged in and out.

PATIENTS

1306 Transferred LT. Francis M. THOMAS, USN, 414336, to U. S. Naval Hospital, Portsmouth, Va. for treatment. Diagnosis: ______.

Note: Patients transferred with expected length of absence over 30 days or when ship is sailing outside of continental U. S. waters, should be logged. Diagnosis should be included if known.

PERSONAL EFFECTS

1310 Personal effects of the late JONES, Paul M., 146

14 41, SN, USN, were inventoried and forwarded to ______.

PERSONNEL

Absentees

0800 Mustered the crew (at quarters) (at foul weather parade) (on station) (at quarters for Captain's inspection). Absentees: (none) (DOE, J. Q., 321 14 21, SA, USN, absent without authority from (muster); GISH, W. T., 427 44 31, RM3, USNR, AWOL since 0700 this date; JONES, M. C., 214 04 16, QM3, USN, AWOL since 0930 15 April 1954; ARCHER, H. C., 639 50 13, FA, USN, AWOL since 0730, 3 April 1954, was this date declared a deserter from this vessel, having been AWOL for a period of thirty (30) days).

Note: There is no legal distinction between absence over leave and absence without leave. All are logged as absence without leave or AWOL. In the case of a man's continued absence, the fact of his absence should be logged once daily, preferably following 0800 muster, until the man returns, is declared a deserter, or is otherwise transferred or detached from the ship or station.

0900 A systematic search of entire ship for DOE, J. Q., 321 14 21, SA, USN, who missed 0800 muster disclosed that (he was not on board) (he was found to be sleeping in the bos'n locker—Comp. A-301-A).

1000 RecSta, NORVA, dispatch 031600Z reports that JONES, M. C., 214 04 16, QM3, USN, AWOL since 0930, 15 April 1954 returned to Naval custody and was being held at that station pending disposition of charges.

Note: Such an entry reflects that an absentee has returned to Naval jurisdiction and that further entries relative to the absence involved are unnecessary.

Return of

2200 DOE, J. J., 321 41 61, QM3, USN, returned on board (was delivered on board by the Shore Patrol,

Norfolk, Virginia), having been AWOL since 0745 this date.

2300 GISH, W. T., 427 44 31, RM3, USN, AWOL since 0700 this date, was delivered under guard from the Receiving Station, Boston, Mass., accused of drunk and disorderly conduct at that station. By order of the Commanding Officer, he was restricted to limits of ship pending disposition of charges.

Note: For entries regarding placing under arrest or in confinement, see Prisoners.

Boards

0800 The Naval Examining Board (Supervisory Board) (Board of Investigation), CAPT. A. B. SEA, USN, Senior Member, appointed by ComBatCruLant serial ______ of April ______ met in the case of LT Xavier Y. ZEE, USN, 426514.

0900 The Naval Examining Board in the case of LT Xavier Y. ZEE, USN, 426514, adjourned until 0800 1 March-______ (to await the action of the convening authority).

Courts of Inquiry

1000 The Court of Inquiry, CAPT A. B. SEA, USN, Senior Member, appointed by ComCruDesPac serial 2634 of 2 April ______ met in the case of the late JONES, P. M., 416 41 14, SN, USN.

1030 The Court of Inquiry in the case of the late JONES, P. M., 416 41 14, SN, USN adjourned to meet ashore at the scene of death.

Special Courts-Martial

1000 The Special Court-Martial, CDR J. Q. DOE, USN, Senior Member, appointed by the Commanding Officer, serial 123 of May ______ met in the case of DOE, J. J., 423 77 62, SA, USN.

1200 The Special Court-Martial which met in the case

of DOE, J. J., 423 77 62, SA, USN, recessed to meet again at 1300 this date.

Note: A court "adjourns" if it will not meet again that date; if it meets again the same date it "recesses." If known the date and time of next meeting is logged.

Summary Courts-Martial

0900 The Summary Court-Martial, CDR X. Y. ZEE, USN, opened at 0800 in the case of DOE, J. J., 423 77 62, SA, USN (and adjourned at 0900 to await the action of the convening authority).

1100 The Summary Court-Martial in the case of DOE, J. J., 423 77 62, SA, USN, adjourned to await the action of the convening authority.

Deaths

0416 SEA, William P., 176 45 43, GM1, USN, died on board as a result of ______.

Deserters

0800 JONES, H. A., 621 73 18, BM2, USN, was this date declared a deserter from this vessel, having been AWOL since 0800 1 May 1953, a period of thirty days.

Discharges

1000 WATTS, John M., 462 13 62, BMC, USN, was discharged from the Naval service in order to re-enlist on board.

Injuries

1035 During drill on the 5″ loading machine MOE, J. A., 631 42 91, SN, USN, received a compound fracture of the right foot when a drill shell fell on his foot; not due to his own misconduct. Treatment administered by the Medical Officer. Disposition: placed on sick list.

Note: In order to protect the Government from false claims and to furnish a record for honest claimants, it is important that accurate and complete entry, including all pertinent details, be made of each and every injury, accident, or casualty, however slight, among the officers, crew, visitors, or passengers.

Mast Reports

1500 The Commanding Officer held mast and imposed non-judicial punishment as follows: SMITH, R. N., 304 52 07, SA, USN. OFFENSE: Disobedience of an order and shirking duty on 3 July 1953. PUNISHMENT: Extra duties of two (2) hours a day for ten (10) days commencing 5 July.

KEYS, E. R., 499 63 07, FN, USN, OFFENSE: AWOL from 1 July 1953 to 2 July 1953, a period of one (1) day, three (3) hours and thirty (30) minutes. PUNISHMENT: Restriction to the limits of ship for ten (10) days commencing 5 July 1953.

PRISONERS

1122 WILLIAM, T. M., 427 31 62, SA, USN, accused of disobedience of orders of the Commanding Officer on this date and was restricted to limits of ship by order of the Commanding Officer pending disposition of charges.

1200 CLARK, R. T., 734 95 74, BM3, USN, returned on board in an intoxicated condition and after medical examination was placed in confinement for safekeeping by order of the Commanding Officer.

0900 CLARK, R. T., 734 95 74, BM3, USN, was released from confinement for safekeeping and restored to duty by order of the Commanding Officer.

0900 WILLIAMS, A. M., 246 76 13, SA, USN, was released from confinement and brought to Captain's Mast.

1445 Pursuant to the orders of the Commanding Officer, NOBLE, C. T., 999 01 64, EMFA, USN, was placed in confinement on bread and water for three (3) days in execution of non-judicial punishment assigned him at mast on this date.

2250 HATCH, W. T., 413 70 47, QM3, USN, was returned on board by Portsmouth Civil Authorities after being arrested on a charge of "assault with an automobile." He is held in custody of the Commanding Officer to await trial in City Traffic Court, Portsmouth, Va., at 1100 18 March ———.

1630 By order of the Commanding Officer, HATCH, W. T., PVT, 1888830, USMC, was released from confinement and restored to duty, following completion of the period of confinement adjudged by sentence of summary court-martial.

RE-ENLISTMENTS

1000 WATTS, Kenneth M., 364 14 63, BMC, USN, reenlisted for a period of 4 years (extended his enlistment for a period of 2 years).

SENTENCE

1534 DOAKES, J. D., 756 32 44, SA, USN, was convicted on 30 April 1954 by special court-martial of a charge of assaulting SMITH, M. R., 222 75 24, SN, USN, on 13 April 1954 in violation of Article 128, UCMJ.

SENTENCE.—To forfeit fifty-six dollars ($56) a month for three (3) months and to be confined at hard labor for three (3) months. The Commanding Officer as convening authority approved and ordered executed only so much of this sentence as provides for forfeiture of fifty-six dollars ($56) a month for one (1) month and confinement at hard labor for one (1) month. The brig of this ship is designated as the place of confinement.

SHIP MOVEMENTS

1100 (U.S.S.) WILKES-BARRE (CL 103) got underway and stood out of the harbor.

1130 (U.S.S.) BELTRAMI (AK 162) stood into the

harbor and anchored (in Berth D-3) (moored alongside Pier 4).

1300 (U.S.S.) HARLAN R. DICKSON (DD 708) got underway from alongside this vessel and anchored in Berth D-8.

1600 (U.S.S.) REMEY (DD 688) stood in and moored alongside (to port) (outboard) of (U.S.S.) BELTRAMI (AK 162).

SHIPS PRESENT

Ships present: (U.S.S.) MISSOURI (BB 63) (ComBatCruLant embarked), (U.S.S.) TARAWA, (CVA 40) (ComCarDiv 2 embarked), (U.S.S.) IOWA (BB 61), and various units of the U. S. Atlantic Fleet, yard and district craft. SOPA is ComBatCruLant in (U.S.S.) MISSOURI (BB 63).

Ships Present: Task Group 63.1 less DesDiv 12 plus (U.S.S.) MACON (CA 132) and various units of the British and French Navies. SOPA is ComCarDiv 4 (CTG 63.1) in (U.S.S.) MIDWAY (CVA 41).

SHORE PATROL

1300 Pursuant to orders of the Commanding Officer, JONES, Q. T., 786 89 67, QM2, USN, in charge of 17 men, left the ship to report to Senior Shore Patrol Officer, Norfolk, Va., for temporary duty (or TAD).

0200 The Shore Patrol detail with JONES, Q. T., 786 89 67, QM2, USN, in charge returned to the ship.

Chapter V

COMMUNICATIONS

Communications are essential to the exercise of command. Since, on relieving the watch, the Officer of the Deck has assumed many of the responsibilities of command, he must know enough about all forms of communications to discharge his duties efficiently.

INTERNAL

The first general classification for communication equipment and knowledge may be termed "internal" or "interior." It has to do with the ship itself and provides the means for informing and directing the ship's company. In its entirety it is a complicated subject, mastered only by those specialists responsible for its maintenance. But, insofar as it relates to the duties of the Officer of the Deck, internal communications employs a relatively limited number of circuits and types of equipment.

The Officer of the Deck should know in detail the internal communication facilities installed in the bridge-pilothouse area. At first the number of sound-powered telephone circuits may be appalling, but it will soon be evident that many of them are used for some special purpose. The major ones, such as the JA (the Captain's command circuit), are the ones most commonly used. Remember that *where* they go and *who* mans them and *when* are important details. The proper voice procedure to use on a sound-powered telephone should be known and used. It can be found in the *Fleet Telephone Talkers Manual.* This telephone procedure is different in some respects from voice radio procedure. An Officer of the Deck must know both procedures and should enforce their usage at all times. It may appear unimportant to you at first that a great variety of homemade conversation is being passed over the sound-powered telephones, but it will be evident when an emergency arises that only trained talkers, using standard phraseology, can get the correct word from station to station. The ship that permits any originality over its telephones is not only incapable of topnotch performance in an emergency, but is liable to experience confusion and mistakes during routine operations.

The intercommunication voice (MC) units, or "squawk-boxes," installed in important stations of most ships are another vital means for passing information. They are normally used by officers and should be limited to emergency business if paralleled by sound-powered telephones. Here again circuit discipline and correct procedure must be enforced by the Officer of the Deck. In order to avoid confusion and speed up transmissions, the standard sound-powered phone talker's procedure mentioned above is modified for use on the MC circuits. Since there is no test of communications, the addressee will be identified, followed by the call of the originator, and, without waiting for an acknowledgement, the originator will deliver the complete message. "Combat, Conn. We are unable to call you on the JA circuit. Check your phones. Over." However, in order that the receiving station may know when the message is finished, all messages must be ended with either "Over" (when the originator desires an acknowledgement for the message) or "out." However, when "aye, aye," is the end of a transmission or when the station selector switch is turned off, it will not be necessary to end the transmission with either "over" or "out."

Passing the Word

"His (the officer of the deck's) orders shall be issued in the customary phraseology of the Service."—*U. S. Navy Regulations, 1948* (Art. 1005).

While this subject has been discussed in an earlier

chapter, it is considered important enough to justify some slight repetition. It is in the use of the general announcing system (1MC) that an Officer of the Deck can establish most decidedly the tone and smartness of his watch. First of all, require that each use of the general announcing system be referred to you for permission. If it is a routine word, such as "Pipe to dinner," you need only be sure that the standard phrase or expression is used or, in some cases, that just the boatswain's call is sounded (See list at the end of this chapter). If the word to be passed is not routine, be sure that there is good reason for using the general announcing system. Having certain individuals paged is certainly never justified unless a real emergency exists. Passing the word for a small group is similarly not advisable, yet many ships resound all day with pleas for "the five-man working party from the B division to lay up to the quarter-deck." It is much better to have someone search out the persons concerned than to abuse the ears of all the ship's company.

In passing the word the Officer of the Deck should be meticulous in using standard, seamanlike phraseology. The term *all hands,* for example, means just that: all men and officers aboard ship. "All hands, man your battle stations" is correct. "All hands, shift into the uniform of the day" is similarly correct and should be enforced. If certain personnel are excepted, they should be listed—"All those not on watch shift into the uniform of the day," for example. The most common abuse of "all hands" is its use when "all those" is meant; for example, "All those taking typhoid shots lay down to sick bay" is correct. Be brief, as in using: "Mail call," instead of "Mail call. All division mail petty officers lay down to the post office and draw mail."

Know the difference between *secure, retreat,* and *pipe down. Secure* means to stop, as: "Secure from fire drill." This means to stop fire drilling and to put away the gear. *Retreat* means to leave a formation or inspection, as:

"Retreat from quarters." This word is passed after *Secure. Pipe down* means strike below, as: "Pipe down aired bedding."

Use of Alarms, Bells, Whistles, and Sirens

The general alarm is a distinctive sound signal of a pulsating ringing tone which should only be used for one purpose: to call all hands to their general quarters stations—as, for example, for an actual fire or collision. The only other time it should be sounded is when it is tested at frequent scheduled intervals. For exercise general quarters or for morning and evening alerts, only the word should be passed. As a result of this policy, the general alarm will mean a *genuine emergency,* and all hands will move on the double.

The chemical alarm is a distinctive 1000-cycle steady tone used only for warning of impending gas or atomic attack.

The ship's bell is used for sounding fog signals at anchor. The bell is rung rapidly for not less than five seconds, followed by the number of strokes necessary to indicate the last two digits of the ship's hull number. As part of the fire alarm, in addition to passing the word, the ship's bell is rung rapidly for at least five seconds, followed by one, two, or three rings to indicate the location of the fire forward, amidships, or aft respectively. Another use of the bell is the traditional one of keeping time. When prescribed, the bell is sounded on the hour and the half hour, following the motion of the senior officer present, from reveille or "up all idlers" until taps.

Boat Gongs

Boat gongs are sounded in port on some ships to indicate the prospective departure of officers' boats and the arrival or departure of visiting officers, unit commanders embarked, and the Commanding Officer. The gongs should be sounded in time to make the departure known. As a boat signal, the gongs are sounded *three* times ten minutes before departure of the boat; *twice when there are* five minutes to go; and *once* with one or two minutes to go before the boat leaves.

When used to indicate the arrival or departure of officers, the gongs are sounded in pairs, the same number as the side boys the officer rates, followed by the name of the officer's command or by the word "staff." Gongs, when used this way, are not honors but are merely for the convenience of those concerned aboard ship.

EXTERNAL COMMUNICATIONS

> "The officer of the deck shall make no official signals except to warn others in company of immediate danger, or as otherwise authorized by the commanding officer."—*U. S. Navy Regulations, 1948* (Art. 1015).

It is also important that the Officer of the Deck be familiar with those facilities, directives, and procedures that concern communicating with other ships, units, or forces ashore. Start off with a general understanding of the communication plan under which the ship is operating. This is a complicated directive, but certain broad aspects can be grasped by the Officer of the Deck with little difficulty. Know what circuits are being manned, who is on those circuits, who has the Fox guard for your ship, or what ships, if any, are dependent on you for their schedules. The technical aspects of frequencies, calls, and authenticators need concern you only insofar as they pertain to matters under your cognizance, such as voice radio circuits.

The Officer of the Deck should be familiar with the communication facilities he has on the bridge. Of these, voice radio is a major one. Know correct voice radio procedure, such as the exact use of "over," "out," "wilco," and "acknowledge." Remember that many people are listening—some of them senior officers who will evaluate your performance. Few things mark a smart ship more firmly than a brisk, correct, and seamanlike use of voice radio.

Visual communications, including flashing light, semaphore, and flag signals, play a large part in the daily work of an Officer of the Deck. Whether or not you are a proficient signalman, you must know enough of the techniques of visual communications to supervise the watch and to insure topnotch performance. This means that you should be able to tell when someone is calling you by light. It also means that you should be able to translate the heading of a message by glancing at the signalman's rough copy and noting who the originator is, who the message is addressed to, what the precedence is, etc.

The use of flag signals is another important aspect of bridge communications. Here again you need not be as familiar with the signal book as the Signal Officer or Flag Lieutenant, but you will need a sound working knowledge if you are to do your job correctly. There will be occasions when you may not even have a competent petty officer to assist you, and the need for reading and looking up a signal quickly and accurately should not embarrass you. It follows, of course, that a similar grasp of the effective tactical publications is also needed by the Officer of the Deck. A quiet morning watch might become very hot indeed if a signal addressed to your ship to perform a certain evolution is not answered promptly. There may be no one on the bridge to assist you; in that case you may have to look up the meaning of the signal and then check on the action required, all in a minute or so.

EXAMPLES OF COMMONLY PASSED WORDS

Many words "vocally" passed aboard smaller ships are sounded by the bugle on larger ships and at the larger shore stations. Some of these bugle calls are: "reveille," "attention to orders," "mess call," "belay," "evening colors," and "taps." In all, more than 100 bugle calls are used in the Navy.

Many ships of medium size have boatswain's mates (or men skilled with the boatswain's pipe) on watch a greater part of the time. These men preface their passing of the word with the more common boatswain's calls. Among these are: "all hands," "pipe down," "mess gear," and "attention" (or "passing the word" or "word to be passed"—identical calls under different names). Many ships preface the word about to be passed with "now hear this," or "now hear there." These three words serve to prepare the listeners for an announcement. A sudden announcement with no preface is too abrupt for many people. They would comprehend only the latter part of the message. If the boatswain's call is used, there is no reason to use a preface such as, "now hear this."

Few ships use the general announcing system between taps and reveille except for emergencies. The call "all hands" is piped before passing the word concerning drills and emergencies. The call "attention" is usually passed before miscellaneous words.

Event	**Word to Be Passed**
AIR BEDDING	"All divisions air bedding."
AIR DEFENSE	"Air defense. Air defense, man all air defense stations."
BOATS	"Away the gig (barge) (No. 1 motor whale boat), away."
CHURCH CALL	"Divine services are being held on the fantail. Maintain quiet about the decks during divine services."
COLLISION	"Collision. Collision, port side, frame twenty" (or other location).

Event	Word to Be Passed
EIGHT O'CLOCK REPORTS	"On deck all eight o'clock reports" (never the "twenty hundred reports").
EXTRA DUTY MEN	"Lay up to the quarter-deck for muster, all extra duty men" (or other special group).
FIRE	"Fire. Fire, compartment A-205-L" (or other location), including deck, frame, and side).
FLIGHT QUARTERS	"Flight quarters. Flight quarters, man all flight quarters stations to launch (recover) aircraft (helicopters)."
FIRE AND RESCUE	"Away fire and rescue party, first (second) (third) section."
GENERAL QUARTERS	"General quarters. General quarters, man all (or your) battle stations."
HOIST IN BOATS	"4th division stand by to hoist (in or out) number ———— motor launch (or gig). (First pipe "Hook on").
IDLERS	"Up all idlers."
INSPECTION (PERSONNEL)	"All hands to quarters for Captain's personnel inspection."
INSPECTION (MATERIAL)	"Stand by all lower deck and topside spaces for inspection."
KNOCK OFF WORK (BEFORE EVENING MEAL)	"Knock off all ship's work. Shift into the uniform of the day." (First pipe "All hands.")
KNOCK OFF WORK (BEFORE NOON MEAL)	"Knock off all ship's work." (First pipe "All hands.")
LATE BUNKS	"Up all late bunks."
LIBERTY	"Liberty to commence for the (first) and (third) sections at 1600; to expire on board at 0745 Friday, 26th February."

Event	Word to be Passed
MAIL	"Mail call."
MEALS	"All hands, pipe to breakfast (noon meal or dinner) (evening meal or supper.") (First pipe "Mess call.")
MESS GEAR (CALL)	"Mess gear (call). Clear the (all) mess decks." (First pipe "Mess call.")
MISTAKE OR ERROR	"Belay that last word."
MUSTER ON STATIONS	"All divisions muster on stations."
PAY	"The crew is now being paid in the mess hall. Line up in alphabetical order."
PREPARATIONS FOR GETTING UNDERWAY	"Make all preparations for getting underway."
QUARTERS FOR MUSTER (REGULAR PARADE)	"All hands to quarters for muster."
QUARTERS FOR MUSTER (INCLEMENT WEATHER)	"All hands to quarters for muster. Foul weather parade." (First pipe "All hands.")
RAIN SQUALL (BEFORE)	"Haul over all hatch hoods and gun covers."
RAIN SQUALL (AFTER)	"Dry down all weather decks."
READINESS FOR GETTING UNDERWAY REPORTS	"All departments, make readiness for getting underway reports to the Officer of the Deck on the bridge."
RELIEVING THE WATCH	"Relieve the watch. On deck the first (second) (third) section. Lifeboat crew on deck to muster." (First pipe "Attention.") "Relieve the wheel and lookouts."
REVEILLE	"Reveille. Reveille, all hands heave out and trice (lash) up."

Event	Word to be Passed
	Or "Reveille. Up all hands. Trice up all bunks." (First pipe "All hands.") (*Reveille is not sounded underway.*)
SHIFTING THE WATCH	"The Officer of the Deck is shifting his watch to the bridge (or quarter-deck)."
SIDE BOYS	"Lay up on the quarter-deck, the side boys."
SMOKING	"The smoking lamp is lighted." (Unless the word applies to the whole ship, the location should be specified).
SPECIAL SEA DETAIL	"Go to (man) your stations, all the special sea detail." Or "Station the special sea detail."
SWEEPERS	"Sweepers, start (man) your brooms. Make a clean sweep down fore and aft." (First pipe "Sweepers.")
TAPS	"Taps. Lights out. All hands turn in to your bunks and keep silence about the decks. Smoking lamp is out in all living spaces." (First pipe "Pipe down.")
TURN TO	"Turn to. (Scrub down all weather decks) (Scrub all canvas) (Sweep down compartments) (Dump trash)."
UNDERWAY	See PREPARATIONS and READINESS

PART TWO

DUTIES OF THE OFFICER OF THE DECK UNDERWAY

Chapter VI

THE WATCH UNDERWAY

"An officer in charge of a watch shall be responsible for the proper performance of all duties prescribed for his watch, and all persons on watch under him shall be subject to his orders."—*U. S. Navy Regulations, 1948.* (Art. 1005).

The Officer of the Deck underway has tremendous responsibilities, matched by wide authority. He is required to expend much energy and to demonstrate considerable intelligence in order to perform his duties efficiently. He is rewarded, however, not only by a sense of personal satisfaction, but by the respect of his fellow officers. Short of command itself there is no finer goal for a young officer to strive for than that of being qualified as a top watchstander underway.

PREPARATION FOR RELIEVING THE WATCH

The subject of preparing for and relieving the watch was covered in general terms in Part One. There are additional matters to be considered, however, when dealing with the specific duties of an Officer of the Deck under way.

It is important to your efficiency while on watch that you make certain physical preparations. Naturally you should wear warm, comfortable clothing; draw foul weather gear, if necessary. Equip yourself with a flashlight and a good pair of binoculars. Ask the quartermaster for a stopwatch if you need one to time navigational lights. (All navigational lights sighted for the first time should be timed for positive identification.)

The following is a partial list of the information that should be obtained before relieving the deck. Experience or special circumstances will suggest additional items.

Navigational Information

(1) The position of the ship on the chart, and how and when determined
(2) Course and speed of the ship
(3) Land or aids to navigation in sight or expected
(4) Changes of course and speed ordered, and by whom, and any such changes that are expected
(5) The depth of water, if on soundings
(6) Sonar conditions
(7) Navigational equipment in use, including loran, radars, sonar, fathometer, radio, etc.
(8) Weather expected (condition of the barometer and the trend of the barometer readings)
(9) Current (set) experienced or expected
(10) Direction of true and relative wind
(11) Aircraft launching (recovery) course
(12) Navigational hazards to be considered, danger bearings, etc.

Tactical Information

(1) Operation plans, orders, etc., under which operating
(2) The formation or disposition prescribed
(3) Own ship's assigned station
(4) Identity and location of the guide and the OTC
(5) For single and multiple line formations, the prescribed order and distance
(6) For all dispositions and formations, the stations of all ships and/or units, formation or disposition axis, and screen axis
(7) The zigzag plan in effect
(8) Formation course (true, by gyro, and by magnetic compass)

(9) Speed: signalled speed or normal speed, and the speed then being made; positioning speed
(10) Station keeping data: amount and frequency of changes in revolutions to keep station, as well as amount of rudder (if any) being carried
(11) Radar and radio guards assigned
(12) Recognition data
(13) Tactical circuits manned and who mans them (CIC or conn), with voice calls of OTC, own ship, and ships in formation, including screen
(14) Information of enemy, including unidentified air and surface contacts on radar screen
(15) Status of air defense measures, including combat air patrol
(16) Airborne early warning information
(17) Radar guards
(18) Flight operations scheduled or in progress
(19) Pertinent facts concerning ships in company, eccentric movements, known unfamiliarity with Allied procedures, radars inoperative, etc.

Ship Information

(1) Condition of readiness and material condition set
(2) Status of lookouts, sea details, and the watch on deck
(3) Lifeboats ready
(4) The condition of ground tackle
(5) Status of the watch being relieved
(6) Boilers in use, and anticipated speed changes. Reserve speed available. Maximum speed requirements
(7) Important engineering machinery, electronic equipment, or gunnery equipment out of commission, and the status of repair work
(8) Important events scheduled by the plan of the day to take place during the watch

(9) Any outstanding or unexecuted orders
(10) The location of the Captain and Navigator (and, if a flagship, the Admiral, his Chief of Staff, and his staff duty officer)
(11) Officer who has the conn.

Read the current message file board before relieving, as far back as your last watch. Note weather forecasts in particular. If there are storms in your general area, such as hurricanes, plot their predicted tracks. One of the attributes of a good naval officer and seaman is weather wisdom. Know what weather is to be expected and plan ahead accordingly. If heavy weather is anticipated, take steps to inform the crew and to implement the heavy weather bill. Junior officers should remember that their seniors, particularly the Commanding Officer, are always vitally interested in weather. A visit to CIC before reporting topside to relieve will inform you of the tactical situation.

In preparation for night watches, the Captain's night order book is of major importance. It must be read carefully and initialed by the Officer of the Deck, Junior Officer of the Watch, and the CIC watch officer. The standing orders that are a part of the night order book should also be read again each time before taking over a night watch.

Dark Adaptation

Another special step in preparing for a watch at night is to become dark adapted before relieving the deck. This is done by staying in a part of the ship that is "rigged for red" before going on watch, or by wearing special goggles. The result of both of these procedures is the exposure of your eyes to red light only, before going on watch. This will not result in perfect dark adaptation but will help speed the process sufficiently so that by the time you actually relieve the deck you should have good night vision. It is assumed, of course, that there are no bright or white lights visible in the pilothouse or on the bridge. There will be more on this subject farther along in Chapter VIII.

RELIEVING THE WATCH

After making all reasonable preparations, you are now ready to get your oral turnover after informing your predecessor that you are ready to relieve him. This is a critical period, since the whole watch is usually being relieved at the same time, to say nothing of the same procedure going on in other ships in the formation. Do not divert the attention of the officer you are relieving from his duties if the watch is busy. You can always use an extra few minutes on the bridge getting oriented.

Before you say the irrevocable words: "I relieve you," be certain that you understand the situation. Check on the status of the watch; know what progress has been made in their relief.

After relieving, report the fact to the Commanding Officer and/or the Command (Supervisory) Watch Officer (if either is on the bridge).

ORGANIZING THE WATCH

Upon taking over the deck, the first item on the agenda should be to organize your watch. This means, first of all, checking each important or key man to be sure that he knows what is expected of him. Too often an untrained or partially trained man will be jammed into the watch bill because of an oversight or of necessity, and such a man will likely not be noticed until he has made a mistake or has failed in his duties. If you do not recognize the men on watch with you as qualified and experienced, by all means check on their qualifications. On-the-spot instruction by the JOOW or an experienced petty officer might be sufficient to enable them to stand a watch. If you have any serious doubts about their qualifications, however, do not hesitate to refer the matter to the senior watch officer (in the case of officers) or to the division officer concerned. A green lookout or an unqualified steersman can get you into serious trouble.

Another source of potential trouble is a noisy bridge. Important voice radio messages or reports over interior communication circuits may be missed if the noise level is high. Unofficial conversation in low tones may be permitted (not for the steersman, however), except under circumstances of tension and exceptional alertness, such as steaming darkened in formation.

It is advisable to organize your bridge personnel so that everyone has specific duties, such as answering telephones or call bells, leaving you partially free from administrative detail. An officer or experienced enlisted man familiar with correct voice radio procedure can be detailed to answer on the bridge voice radio circuits when your ship is called. The primary tactical voice circuit, however, requires your personal attention.

There are many other details too numerous to mention here that should be specifically delegated. The point in all of this meticulous organization is that the Officer of the Deck can never justifiably tie himself down to a succession of small tasks when his major responsibilities concern the efficient operation and safety of the whole ship. The Officer of the Deck should normally be looking out in the direction in which the ship is moving and should not have his head buried in the pilothouse answering some phone.

There are certain details, however, that the Officer of the Deck should handle himself. These are such items as the master switch for the ship's running lights, all the emergency alarm devices, and the phone or voice tube to the Commanding Officer's emergency cabin. The Officer of the Deck should also know the exact procedure in handling a steering casualty.

THE CONN[1]

"The officer of the deck is the officer on watch in charge of the ship. He shall be responsible for the safety of the ship and for the performance of the duties prescribed in these regulations and by the commanding officer. Every person on board who is subject to the orders of the commanding officer, except the executive officer, and those other officers specified in article 1009, shall be subordinate to the Officer of the Deck."—*U.S. Navy Regulations, 1948* (Art. 1008).

To *conn* means to control, or direct by rudder and engine order telegraph, the movements of a ship. As Officer of the Deck you normally have both the deck and the conn. It is customary for Commanding Officers of most U. S. naval vessels to take the conn at times when intricate or dangerous maneuvers are to be performed. It is also customary for Officers of the Deck to assist in such maneuvers by checking the performance of duty of members of the bridge watch and by keeping a watchful eye on the entire maneuver in order to inform the Commanding Officer of anything which might escape his notice and which consequently might endanger the safety of the ship. Likewise, when the Officer of the Deck has the conn during delicate maneuvers or in restricted waters, the Commanding Officer is customarily on the bridge watching the over-all picture to guard against mishap. In effect then, there is a two-intellect system in which one human being has the conn, giving all orders to the wheel and the engines, and another human being is assisting and advising. By careful observation and prudent advice the latter endeavors to prevent an accident which might result from

[1] Based on a letter promulgated by the Commander-in-Chief, Atlantic Fleet.

a momentary lapse of memory or an oversight on the part of the person conning.

Navy Regulations, 1948, in chapters 7 (sec. 2) and 10 (sec. 2), establish a bridge organization which provides this safeguard, in which one human intellect supplements another, by assigning to both the Commanding Officer and the Officer of the Deck definite responsibility for the safety of the ship, regardless of which person has the conn. In fact the word *conn* does not appear in *Navy Regulations,* and no direct statement is made as to the duties of the Officer of the Deck when another person is exercising control of the ship's movement—a matter in which he has considerable legal interest.

The following basic principles have long been accepted by experienced sea-going naval officers:

(a) One and only one person can give orders to the wheel and to the engine order telegraph at any one time.

(b) The identity of the person giving these orders must be known to the personnel on the bridge.

(c) The Officer of the Deck may be relieved of the conn by another officer, but retains a considerable measure of responsibility for the ship's safety.

(d) The Commanding Officer may take over the deck, or he may take over the conn. In the former case the Officer of the Deck has no legal responsibility for the safety of the ship except as specifically detailed by the Commanding Officer. But when the Commanding Officer takes over the conn, the Officer of the Deck carries out all the duties assigned to him by *Navy Regulations,* assisting and advising the Commanding Officer.

(e) In taking the conn from the Officer of the Deck, the Captain should do so formally, in such a manner that all personnel of the bridge watch will be notified, unless emergency action is required. In the latter case the issuing of an order direct to the wheel or engine order telegraph will, in itself, constitute assumption of responsibility for directing the ship's movements. When taking the conn in this manner the Commanding Officer will then retain the conn until he formally turns it over to another person.

(f) Each Commanding Officer establishes a procedure by which positive indication is given by him whenever he has assumed direct control of the ship and thereby relieved the conning officer of all responsibilities for such control. The procedure for delegating responsibility for control of the ship to a conning officer must be equally positive.

The Officer of the Deck has no problem to solve if the above well recognized principles are observed at all times in his ship. But even the best of Commanding Officers is a fallible human being and may, while concentrating on the vital matters at hand, neglect to follow the recommended procedure in taking over or relinquishing the conn. Under these circumstances it is up to the Officer of the Deck to understand his Commanding Officer's actions and to clarify the situation with a polite: "Do you have the conn, sir?" or "I have the conn, sir." Then see that important bridge personnel know who has the conn.

When the OOD does not have the conn he assists the conning officer in many specific ways. One of the most important is to insure that the orders from the conning officer are *understood and acted upon correctly* by the steersman and other bridge personnel. In addition, he should make sure that the conning officer knows that his orders are being executed. Under conditions of high noise level this is sometimes difficult. In addition the Officer of the Deck may take station where he can best assist the conning officer in maintaining a lookout.

REPORTS BY THE OFFICER OF THE DECK

"The officer of the deck shall promptly report to the commanding officer all matters which affect or which may affect the safety of the ship or personnel, or ships in company. All land, shoals, rocks, lighthouses, beacons, buoys, discolored water, vessels, aircraft, or wrecks detected; any marked changes in the barometer, force or direction of the wind, state of the sea, or indications or warnings of storm or bad weather; all changes of formation, course, or speed ordered by the officer in tactical command, or changes of course or speed made by the ships in company or by himself; derangements to equipment which may affect the safety or operations of the ship; all serious accidents; the winding of the chronometers; the hours 0800, 1200, and 2000; and, in general, all occurrences worthy of notice of the commanding officer shall be reported to him, subject to his orders. When a flag officer is embarked, similar reports shall also be made to him, subject to his orders."—*U. S. Navy Regulations, 1948* (Art. 1020).

Little need be added to the above directive. There is one point, however, that often confuses junior officers standing night watches. Should they comply literally with *Navy Regulations* and wake the Captain for every item listed above? The answer is an unqualified affirmative. You have no choice but to obey the letter of the *Regulations*. If the reports are not desired by the Commanding Officer, he may limit you in some arbitrary fashion, depending on the particular circumstances. But until he does, you should be meticulous in making your reports. If there is doubt in your mind, play safe and call the Captain. Do not be concerned with waking the Captain; he is accustomed by now to interrupted sleep when underway at night. He will gain peace of mind and reassurance by your conscientious attention to duty. Be certain that important messages are really understood by a sleeping Commanding Officer. Some people can acknowledge without really awaking.

PILOTS

"A pilot is merely an advisor to the commanding officer. His presence on board shall not relieve the commanding officer or any of his subordinates from their responsibility for the proper performance of the duties with which they may be charged concerning the navigation and handling of the ship."—*U. S. Navy Regulations, 1948* (Art. 0752).

The article partly quoted above goes on to mention certain exceptions to the above principle, notably in the case of pilots in the Panama Canal and when entering a drydock. By and large, a pilot must be considered as an advisor. Even though he takes the conn upon invitation of the Commanding Officer, the Officer of the Deck must not relax his vigilance for the safety of the ship. Pilots are often unfamiliar with the type of ship they are handling. Often they use non-standard commands to the annunciator or to the steersman. The Officer of the Deck should assist the pilot and should cooperate with him fully. In addition he can profitably observe the pilot and thus learn much about ship handling and about local conditions of tide and current. The Officer of the Deck should insure that actions of tugs conform to the pilot's orders.

Among preparations that can be made for a pilot's arrival are: An interpreter (if needed); ladder rigged over the side; and the Junior Officer of the Watch to meet him as he climbs aboard.

Chapter VII

SHIP HANDLING

"The commanding officer of a ship shall afford frequent opportunities to the executive officer, and to other officers of the ship as practicable, to improve their skill in ship handling."—*U.S. Navy Regulations, 1948* (Art. 0754).

The Officer of the Deck may expect to handle the ship in keeping station, in making turns in formation for changes of course, and on other occasions when no great risk is involved. If his Commanding Officer is so disposed, the Officer of the Deck may even handle the ship when making a landing alongside a wharf, pier, or other ship. In any event, the Officer of the Deck must prepare himself by study and observation to handle his ship. Occasions may arise, as they have in the past, in which junior officers must take their ships to sea because of an emergency due to weather or enemy action.

This guide cannot be a definitive textbook on ship handling. It is proposed, however, to outline in this chapter some of the important matters the Officer of the Deck should know. Further study in such standard reference books as *Knight's Modern Seamanship* is recommended.

DEFINITIONS

An Officer who desires to become an efficient ship handler must first know his ship. He should know the following:

Pivot point.—The point of rotation within the ship as she makes a turn. This point is generally about one-third the length of the ship from the bow and fairly close to the bridge (when going ahead).

Turning circle.—The path described by the ship when turning. The turning circle will vary with amounts of rudder and with speeds used.

Advance.—For any turn, the advance is the distance gained in the direction of the original course from the time the rudder is put over until the ship is on the new course.

Transfer.—For any turn, the transfer is the distance gained in a direction perpendicular to that of the original course from the time the rudder is put over until on the new course.

Tactical diameter.—For any amount of constant rudder angle, the tactical diameter is the distance made good in a direction perpendicular to that of the original course line from the time the rudder is put over until the ship is on a reverse heading. It is the transfer for a turn of 180°.

Standard rudder.—Standard rudder is the angle of rudder for that particular ship which under normal conditions will give standard tactical diameter (1500 yards unless otherwise specified.)

Full rudder.—Full rudder is a prescribed angle of rudder for that particular ship (just a few degrees short of the stops) which will give reduced tactical diameter (1200 yards unless otherwise specified).

Acceleration and deceleration rates.—Acceleration and deceleration rates are the rates at which a ship picks up or loses headway after a change of speed.

GENERAL PRINCIPLES

An officer should also know certain general principles and their specific application to his ship, some examples of which are given below.

The effect of the wind upon turning.—Most ships, particularly those with high bows, turn slowly into the wind when going ahead, but more rapidly when turning away from it. Conversely, they will back rapidly into the wind. The effect on a particular ship can be estimated by comparing the "sail area" forward of the pivot point with that abaft the pivot point. If the "sail area" is greater forward, the ship will have the above tendencies. If greater aft, her tendencies will be the opposite; this is particularly true of aircraft carriers. The "sail area" is composed of the fore-and-aft vertical surfaces of the hull and superstructure against which the wind exerts force.

Effect of speed upon turning.—With constant rudder angle, for speeds any appreciable amount above steerageway, any increase in speed will result in an increased turning circle. This is a result of the inertia of the ship, which tends to keep it going in its original direction of motion. This increased turning circle will vary from ship to ship and will be most noticeable when ships of different types are operating together. Since the guide is usually a large ship and will use the same amount of rudder or standard rudder for all speeds, you must know what amount of rudder for your ship will match the turning circle of the guide for the speed at which any turn is made.

For speeds approaching bare steerageway, a decrease in speed will result in an increased turning circle. This is due to the decreased effect of the rudder acting against the inertia of the ship which tends to keep the ship moving in a straight line. In making a turn at low speeds, therefore, an increased amount of rudder is needed. You should always know what is the minimum speed at which you will still have steerageway.

Effect of shallow water.—Reduced space between the ship's hull and the bottom in shallow water prevents the screw currents from flowing freely and from acting upon the hull and rudder in the normal manner. As a result the ship may be sluggish or erratic in answering the rudder. In addition there is a great waste of power, and the speed through the water will be less than that indicated by the propeller revolutions.

Time lag in response to orders.—There is a noticeable lag beween the time an order is given to the wheel or engines and the time that the effect of the response is felt. For example, in order to have your rudder go over at the same spot as that of the ship ahead so that you will turn in her wake, you must give your order to turn when the kick of the preceding ship's rudder is near your bridge.

Backing power available.—The backing power available may be considerably less than the power for going ahead. For the same amount of engine power when backing, slightly less drive will be received from the propeller than when going ahead. This is due to the fact that a propeller is more efficient when turning in the ahead direction. "Back one-third" and "Back two-thirds" normally call for one-third and two-thirds, respectively, of the power available for backing. The turns for "Ahead one-third" and "Ahead two-thirds" are based upon one-third and two-thirds of standard speed. There is a probability that "Ahead one-third (two-thirds)" and "Back one-third (two-thirds)" will not have quite equal effect. As a result, in addition to swinging when one engine is backing and the other going ahead (both at one-third or two-thirds), the ship can be expected to pick up a slight amount of way.

Factors affecting acceleration and deceleration.—The manner in which ships gain and lose headway, carry their way, and respond to changes of engine speed, varies with the size of the ship, her underwater lines, condition of bottom, wind, and state of sea. A heavy ship, a clean-bottom ship, or a ship with fine lines, will tend to hold her way, and vice-versa. A heavy ship, a foul-bottomed ship, or a ship with broad lines, will tend to pick up headway slowly in response to changes of engine speed.

Factors affecting turning.—As Officer of the Deck you

should not only know how to make a normal turn, but how to turn your ship in the shortest time and how to turn it in the shortest space.

The procedures for these two maneuvers are quite different. To turn your ship in the *shortest time,* go ahead with full power and put your rudder hard over just short of the stops. To turn a ship in the *shortest possible space,* you may have to vary your procedure, depending upon the ship itself and, sometimes, upon wind conditions. A ship with twin rudders is the easiest and probably the quickest to turn, and is the least affected by the wind conditions. Simply put the rudders over full in the direction of the desired turn, and keep them there. Ring up "Two-thirds ahead" on the outboard engine and "Two-thirds astern" on the inboard engine. Adjustments in the speed of the inboard engine can be made to keep the ship from going ahead or astern as she turns on her heel.

To turn a single-rudder twin-screw ship in the shortest space is slightly more difficult. If the screws are set well off from the centerline, and if the turn is not adversely affected to any degree by the wind, the turn can be made by going ahead on the outboard engine and backing on the inboard engine. When the wind adversely affects the turn, or when the screws are not sufficiently offset for a good, powerful couple, motion ahead and astern in turn may be necessary to supplement the effect of the rudder. As a general rule, when the ship is going ahead with steerageway, the rudder should be put over in the direction of the desired turn; when the ship is going astern with steerageway, the rudder should be in the opposite direction; when the ship has no way on or less than steerageway, the rudder should be amidships. The amount of way on and the position of the rudder should be carefully watched. Some ships with large single rudders will show a somewhat similar tendency to a twin-rudder ship; that is, to answer to the effect of an ahead-turning screw on the rudder even when they have a small amount of sternway. The Officer of the Deck must know the characteristics of his own ship in this regard.

Turning a single-screw ship in the shortest space is the most complicated maneuver of all. Most ships of this type have right handed propellers. To turn a ship of this type requires some way on. Therefore, to turn in the shortest space, alternate between headway and sternway. Whenever the engine is going ahead, throw the rudder in the direction of the desired turn. Knowing when to shift the rudder after starting the engines backing is a matter of knowing the ship. Normally the rudder should be shifted sometime shortly after the ship loses headway. It should then be kept there until the engine is put ahead.

HANDLING IN FORMATION

Handling a ship in company with others requires a sound knowledge of the effective tactical instructions, and a thorough understanding of the relative motion of ships. Information on the first essential is found in *Allied Naval Maneuvering Instructions*. Every officer standing deck watches at sea should be so familiar with this important directive that he can find at once the proper guidance for any circumstance that may arise involving the movements of his ship. The opening chapters are particularly important, since they provide the basic concepts and definitions upon which all subsequent instructions are based.

The second essential for efficient ship handling in formation—an understanding of relative motion—can be attained by study and practice in working maneuvering board problems. An authoritative reference is the chapter on the maneuvering board in Dutton's *Navigation and Nautical Astronomy*. Many Naval schools provide excellent courses in relative movement, but any officer can become proficient by a moderate amount of study and a good deal of practice. It is recommended that problems be solved both with your own ship at center and with the guide at center. The former method is almost always employed in CIC; the latter is often useful on the bridge, particularly for a vessel in the screen.

An important result of skill in using the maneuvering board is the ability to visualize problems and to solve them mentally. For a complicated evolution, such as taking a new and distant station in a formation, your mental solution would, of course, be only approximate and would be subject to modification by CIC or by a Junior Officer of the Watch who actually works out the problem on paper. But the mental solution permits you to make an instant change of course and speed which expedites the maneuver and demonstrates a ship's smartness and efficiency. For simple problems, such as gaining 10 degrees in bearing on the guide while maintaining distance, the mental solution is sufficient since it is subject to constant confirmation by taking periodic bearings and ranges.

CLOSE STATION KEEPING

The mental process discussed above, of visualizing simple problems in relative motion and solving them correctly, is the key to proficient station keeping in close formation. While it is true that ships do not steam in close formation very often these days, it is still an important requirement, demanded by most type commanders. Patrol and escort vessels, destroyers, cruisers, carriers, and amphibious ships still must, on occasions, be able to steam in column or in line-of-bearing at standard distance, usually darkened at night and at high speed as well.

Steaming in close column demands a keen appreciation of speed and how your ship carries her way. It is largely a matter of speed adjustment.

The stadimeter is an extremely useful instrument when in close formation. Every watch officer should be familiar with its use and should know its capabilities and limitations. It will give readings at closer ranges than will most radars. It is particularly helpful in that it will give you quick and accurate information as to whether you are opening, closing, or holding a steady distance.

Reports of distance should be given with the distance followed by the information as to whether it is "closing," "opening," or "steady." The terms "increasing" or "decreasing" should not be used, as there is chance of confusion with reports concerning bearings.

Develop your sense of distance. Find some spot on the bridge where you can later stand and from which you can line up some object on your ship, such as the jackstaff, with objects on the ship ahead or to the side. When your distance to an adjacent ship has been measured, make a mental note of how the objects aligned for future reference.

There may be times on dark nights when there is not enough light to take stadimeter readings and when you are too close for radar ranges or when radar silence is imposed. Binoculars can then be used to obtain a fair estimate of the distance by judging the amount of the field that the target ship fills. During the day, when you can measure your exact distance to the adjacent ship, look at that ship through binoculars and note the amount of the field that she fills. It takes a lot of practice to become proficient in this use of the binoculars, but it is worth it.

If you are the first ship in the column, or if your ship is the guide, make every effort to ensure good steering and steady speed. Watch the steersman carefully and, at the same time, see that the proper revolutions are actually being made. The Officers of the Deck astern will appreciate your efforts.

When following another ship, the keeping of proper distance depends largely on your ability to detect early indications of opening or closing motion and to make proper speed adjustments to counteract that motion. In this regard you should remember that a ship following in the wake of another requires a few more revolutions than she will in still water to make good the same speed as the ship ahead because of the necessity to overcome the wake turbulence or "kick" of the preceding ship. An erratic steersman who takes you in and out of the wake of the ship ahead will make your problem of speed adjustment a difficult one. Therefore, keep a close watch on your steersman. Make your speed correction with care, remembering that there is a time lag before the effect of change is felt. If you do not allow for this time lag you are liable to correct twice for the same error. That will result in a need for a correction, probably larger, in the opposite direction. Once such surging starts it is hard to stop. Study the time lag of your ship intently until you get to know it. Observe the effect of one correction carefully before applying another. Remember that excessive use of rudder acts as a brake. Always correct the steering before increasing speed.

In general, when in column, keep your ship inside rather than outside the prescribed distance. It is easier to drop back than to close up. Know the allowable tolerances and keep within them. Remember the fellow next astern, and keep your course and speed as steady as possible. The reputation of being a good ship to follow is a difficult one for a ship to earn, but it is worth trying for.

Know your proper station for column open order. The prescribed angles on the quarter of the leader are small, and there is a general tendency to exceed them. Check the angle carefully, and, when on station, call the attention of the steersman to the distance between the ship and the wake of the guide.

When in column, always keep in mind your number in the column and to which side you should sheer out in an emergency. This is the same side as that of your position when in column open order, and it follows the standard pattern—odd ships to starboard, even ships to port. When for any reason you find yourself getting uncomfortably close to the ship ahead, ease your bow out very slightly on the side to which you would sheer out in an emergency.

Course changes for a formation in column may be made in two ways: by individual ships turning together, and by wheeling (changing course in succession, following the ship ahead).

When change of course is made by turning together, be sure to put your rudder over the proper amount promptly on the execution of the signal. Inform the steersman of the new course, and see that he does not swing past it nor use an excessive amount of rudder in meeting the swing. Either of these errors by the steersman will cause you to end up behind bearing in the line of bearing resulting from the maneuver. Keep the nearest ship toward which you are turning under constant visual observation. Check the bearing of the guide as the turn progresses, with a view to detecting promptly any tendency to gain or lose bearing.

In practice, ships do not maintain perfect position, particularly when making frequent simultaneous turns, and the Officer of the Deck must know how to adjust a turn to improve his position. This is largely a question of experience in visualizing the situation, and in looking ahead. Of course, any such adjustments must consider adjacent ships on both sides.

In wheeling, when nearing the turning point of the ship ahead, remember that, when she starts to turn, her stern will swing out, and the inexperienced steersman will, if not cautioned, continue to steer by her stern and thus sheer out. If this happens, you will start your turn *already outside* and will have to make a large turn, both in degrees turned and distance travelled, which will cause you to lose distance. In order to prevent this, if you are properly in station astern of the guide, order the steersman, at the instant the signal for the turn is executed, to steady on course. Specify in your order what that course is. If you are not directly astern of the guide, take a bearing of the guide at the instant the signal is executed, and then order the steersman to steer that as a course. This will ensure your passing through the turning point of the guide.

Presuming that the ship ahead is the guide, or that she has followed the guide properly in her turn, you will attempt to turn in the same water. If the turning point has been correctly approached, the kick (disturbed water) of the rudder of the next ship ahead will be observed to be slightly on your inboard bow. From the kick, the swirl of the wake will arc slightly outboard and then cross the line of advance. Inboard of the wake will be the slick caused by the sliding of the stern of the ship ahead. The inboard edge of the slick will mark the path of her bow; the outboard edge, that of her stern.

Get out on the wing of the bridge where you can see both the ship ahead and the one astern throughout your turn, and thus be in the best position to observe the kick. Stay in that spot until you have made your decision to turn. When the kick of the ship ahead reaches a predetermined position abreast your ship (usually in the vicinity of the bridge), you should give the order to put over the rudder. The exact location of the kick in relation to the bridge will vary in different types of ships, and for any ship will vary with the speed—all of which takes experience to judge.

After the rudder has been put over, your ship will continue straight ahead for a short distance before she starts to swing. Then, if the turn has been correctly timed, she will follow around with the stem just at the inboard edge of the slick of the ship ahead. Normally the outboard edge of the slick of the ship ahead can be lined up with a point on your jackstaff. If the edge draws downward along your jackstaff, the ship is going outside, and if it draws upward, the ship is turning inside.

If the turn is made too late, you will start to go outside of your proper turning circle. If this cannot be corrected immediately by a small amount of increased rudder, the wake of the ship ahead will strike your bow and force you further outside. Under these conditions you should continue to make a standard turn outside and then steady up on the new course, still outside. This course of action is mandatory. When the ship astern has completed her turn, then and only then you may start to ease back into your place in column.

Once your bow is outside the wake of the ship ahead, any attempt to correct this condition by using increased rudder will result in your falling back dangerously on the next ship astern. This is due to the extra distance travelled and to the slowing effect of the large amount of rudder.

If the turn is made too early, you will start to go inside of your proper turning circle. A slight easing of the rudder can correct this. However, this will decrease the slowing effect of your rudder and you will be traveling a shorter distance. Thus you will close up on the next ship ahead. Easing the rudder should therefore be done only when the distance from the next ship ahead is such that these factors will not cause you to come dangerously close. A common error in such cases is to ease the rudder too much, with the result that the ship crosses the wake of the next ship ahead and goes outside. You can avoid this by watching closely for the first indications of turning inside, and then promptly easing the rudder a sufficient amount to check the rate of swing. As soon as this effect has been produced, the rudder should ordinarily be again put over to the standard amount and the turn completed in a normal manner.

The only really dangerous situation in turns arises when a ship is somewhat too close to the ship ahead when making a large change of course. The moment comes when you must choose between more rudder and remaining inside by slowing, stopping, or even backing the inboard engine, or the alternative of easing the rudder and passing under the stern of the ship ahead, and thus going outside her wake. In this situation, resolve any doubts in favor of continuing to turn *inside*. It is safer, and you will eventually regain position quicker. If you hesitate too long and then ease the rudder to go outside, your ship may forge ahead while her bow is still inside the stern of the ship ahead, with possibilities of collision.

If the next ship ahead has turned too soon or too late, instead of following in her wake you should attempt to turn correctly in the wake of the guide. Estimate how much too soon or too late, in terms of distance, the ship ahead made her turn. Then by applying this distance as a correction to the normal position of the kick of the next ship ahead when you make a normal turn, you can still use the kick as a reference point for turning.

As in other maneuvers, the turn in succession may often be used to advantage in correcting the position. When well behind station, boldly cut the corner. If too close, don't turn too soon; turn a bit late, with full rudder.

If the maneuver is executed in fog, or at night, you may not be able to see the kick. As a precaution, therefore, use a stop watch. Start it when the signal is executed. Knowing your distance behind the guide and your speed, you can determine the time when you should arrive at the guide's point of turn. If you have no better information by that time, turn then. If whistle signals are being used and you hear the signal of the next ship ahead, note its time and use it as a new basis for computing the time to turn.

Line of Bearing

When in line of bearing, station keeping is somewhat more complicated, since you are then concerned with both your distance and your bearing. It is in this situation particularly that you will benefit by a thorough understanding of the relative motion of ships. While steaming in close formation, you will rarely have time to plot bearings and distances and obtain a solution if you are not in position. You have to visualize the problem, and then change course and speed properly and promptly as soon as you detect a deviation from your correct bearing and distance.

You can quickly determine whether you are ahead or behind bearing by lining up your alidade on the prescribed bearing of the guide and then sighting through it. If your line of sight falls ahead of the guide, you are ahead; if astern, you are behind.

When the line of ships is a line abreast, a speed that is greater or less than the guide's speed will cause you to advance or retard your bearing with negligible change of range. A slight change of course toward or away from the guide will cause you to close or open range with a slight loss of bearing. A small temporary increase of speed, normally only a few turns, can be used, when desirable, to counteract this small bearing change.

As we have seen, when the line of bearing is a column, the opposite of the above is true. A speed differential will cause you to close or open distance. A change of course will cause a change of bearing with a very slight opening of distance. A small temporary increase of speed can be used, when desirable, to counteract this small distance change.

For lines-of-bearing between these two extremes—line abreast and column—the effects of a course or speed differential are a little more complex.

A combination of course and speed changes is usually required in order to maintain station.

Correct *bearing* is generally considered more important than correct *distance* (errors in bearing are more apparent on the flagship). It is generally considered better to be slightly behind bearing than ahead. It is, of course, best to be accurately on station in both bearing and distance.

When simultaneous turns are made in line-of-bearing, watch the ship toward which the turn is made in order to detect the first sign that she might be turning in the wrong direction.

Open Formations

Handling a ship in the main body of a circular formation is slightly easier than handling a ship in close formation, since normally the ships are not as close. However, since you keep station on a definite bearing from the guide, and at a definite distance, the problems of station keeping are similar to those in line-of-bearing. The only additional problems are in determining what your range and bearing from the guide should be when moving to a new station. CIC can be of great assistance to the Officer of the Deck in these matters.

In order to determine his range and bearing from the guide, the Officer of the Deck must be familiar with the system of plotting formations, using polar coordinates. After plotting the formation, you can easily pick the range and bearing of the guide off the plot. A continuous plot of the formation should be kept so that ordered changes can be quickly translated into terms of new range and bearing from the guide.

Remember that the station numbers given are relative to the formation axis and must be plotted as such. A change in the direction of the formation axis will result in an equal change in the true bearing of your station from the formation center and in your true bearing from the guide.

Remember that the guide is not always at the center. And remember that immediately any signal is executed, the guide is automatically on station, regardless of where she is. This may result in the formation center moving around the guide. If this happens, it causes your station to move a like amount in the same direction.

For any maneuver, determine from a plot your required range and bearing from the guide. Then obtain your actual range and bearing from the guide. Using these figures, determine the course and speed required for you to arrive at your proper station. If there is no change in your proper range and bearing, your problem is, of course, only one of station keeping. A change of formation axis or change in the formation itself will be the only maneuvers that will change your range and/or bearing from the guide unless you are ordered to a new station.

Screening

Handling a ship in a screen is quite similar to handling a ship in the main body of a circular formation. Station keeping problems are the same except that the distances from the guide are greater. The problem of determining range and bearing of your station from the guide is, however, more complex. The Officer of the Deck of a destroyer type ship must be familiar with the maneuvering rules governing screening ships, in addition to the rules governing maneuvers of the various types of formations.

A continuous, up-to-minute plot of the entire formation should be kept, just as for a circular formation, so that any ordered change can be quickly translated into terms of a new range and bearing from the guide.

In order to keep the plot of the screen, you must know

the location of the screen center and the direction of the screen axis. For certain types of screens, the screen center may shift. You must be able to distinguish the signals which will cause such a shift from those that do not. And you must know how to determine the amount and direction of such a shift, and how to allow for it in your maneuver, whether or not a reorientation of the screen is required.

You should keep in mind that in addition to those shiftings of the screen center which are caused by course changes, there are also shiftings of the screen center caused by the rotation of the formation axis. When the formation guide is not at the center of the formation, a shift in the direction of the formation axis will cause the formation center to move relative to the guide. This causes the screen center and all screening stations to move a like amount and in the same direction.

The screen axis may also change. As Officer of the Deck you must know under what conditions it changes without a specific signal to change it, and how to determine its new direction in such cases.

Every effort should be made to start for your new station promptly. A little forehandedness will help toward this end. After each maneuver you should start anticipating the next one. You should check your plot and then determine what will be the minimum change of formation course in each direction that will cause a reorientation in which you will have to change station. And when applicable, you should determine what will be the minimum change of course that will require your initial turn to be in a direction opposite to that of the course change. With these figures firmly in mind, you can quickly translate a signal into action and can start the initial turn while the final solution is still forthcoming.

In working your solutions, be sure that you use the course and speed for the guide that he will actually be following while you are enroute to your station. This is particularly applicable when you start for station prior to the execution of a signal which changes the guide's course and/or speed.

Care must be exercised that maneuvering board solutions do not take you on a course that might endanger other ships of the screen or main body. Before making a turn always ascertain that it is safe to do so.

There are two final points to be made about screening. The first is that normally exact station keeping is not necessary; tolerances are specified in tactical directives. At such times you can afford to devote more time to other matters; perhaps delegating, under supervision, the duty of station keeping to the Junior Officer of the Watch.

The second point is that when reorienting or changing screening station, the Officer of the Deck must keep an alert watch over the whole formation, using his own eyes to a maximum extent. Others can work out maneuvering board solutions to check your quick calculations; your primary job under many conditions is that of chief safety officer.

Chapter VIII

SAFE NAVIGATION

"When at sea, and especially when approaching land or shoal waters, the officer of the deck shall keep himself informed of the position of the ship and of all other particulars which may be of use in keeping the ship out of danger. He shall employ such means and devices as may be available for detecting and avoiding danger from grounding or collision. When there is danger of grounding or collision, he shall take immediate action to minimize and localize any damage which might occur. He shall thoroughly familiarize himself with the laws to prevent collision and shall strictly comply with them. He shall see that the ship is skillfully steered and kept on her course and that when steaming in formation, the assigned station is maintained. He shall see that nothing is done to impair the accuracy of the compasses, and that their errors are frequently verified. During low visibility or when in congested areas he shall station additional lookouts as the circumstances require. He shall see that the lights required by law for preventing collisions are kept burning from sunset till sunrise, except when not in use by orders of competent authority, and that they are inspected half hourly."—*U.S. Navy Regulations, 1948* (Art. 1010).

"Except as prescribed in these regulations or as authorized by the commanding officer, the officer of the deck shall not change the prescribed course or speed of the ship unless necessary to avoid collision or imminent danger."—*U. S. Navy Regulations, 1948* (Art. 1011).

"The commanding officer is responsible for the safe navigation of his ship or aircraft, except as prescribed otherwise in these regulations for ships at a naval shipyard or station, in drydock, or in the Panama Canal. In time of war, or during exercises simulating war, the provisions of this article pertaining to the use of lights and electronic devices may be modified by competent authority.

"The commanding officer of a ship and, as appropriate, of an aircraft, shall:

(d) Keep himself informed of the error of all compasses, and other devices available as aids to navigation.

(i) Insure that efficient devices for fixing the ship's position and for ascertaining the depth of water are employed when underway on soundings, entering or leaving port, or upon approaching an anchorage, shoal, or rock, whether or not a pilot is on board. If circumstances warrant, he shall reduce speed to the extent necessary to permit these devices to be operated efficiently and accurately.

(j) Observe every precaution prescribed by law to prevent collisions and other accidents on the high seas, inland waters, or in the air.

(k) When underway in restricted waters or close inshore, and unless unusual circumstances prevent, steam at a speed which will not endanger other ships or craft, or property close to the shore.

(l) Take special care that the lights required by law to prevent collisions at sea, in port, or in the air are kept in order and burning in all weathers from sunset to sunrise, and require that means for promptly relighting or replacing such lights are available.—*U.S. Navy Regulations, 1948* (Art. 0751).

Young officers are inclined to look upon disasters at sea as something remote from their experience and as events that are as infrequent and as inescapable as being struck by lightning. On the contrary, collisions and groundings are altogether too common and are almost always avoidable. It is true that perfect safety records cannot reasonably be expected of any force or fleet; the business of going to sea even in peacetime is inherently dangerous. The U.S.S. *Hobson* sinking, in which 175 lives were lost, is an example of how dangerous it can be. But the most important aspect of this subject is that collisions and groundings can be avoided in most part by the intelligent application of the fundamental principles of good seamanship and common sense. While unusual material casualties that cannot be immediately coped with do occasionally happen, in most cases some human error has set in motion or abetted the process that leads to an accident.

COLLISION

Analysis of collision cases reveals that one or more of the following factors are frequently involved:

- Failure to establish in time the fact that risk of collision exists
- Failure to take timely avoiding action
- Failure to turn on running lights in the emergency while ships were darkened
- Failure to notify the Commanding Officer of a potentially dangerous situation
- Failure to check for change of bearing until well clear
- Excessive reliance on CIC to the exclusion of a common sense evaluation of the situation on the bridge
- Poor judgment in evaluating the effects of wind and tide
- Failure to understand the tactical characteristics ot the ship
- Injudicious use of the power available in the ship

Bridge and CIC PPI's were both on long scale, thereby making the detection of close-in targets difficult

Bridge personnel did not keep a sharp visual lookout

The organization between CIC and bridge did not insure the receipt of tactical signals by the conning officer

A radical course change was made by one or more ships without informing ships in the vicinity

Whistle signals were not used

The required checks between gyro and magnetic compass were not made

Other ships in the formation observed the merging of pips without broadcasting a warning by voice radio

Maneuvering board solutions provided by CIC were not checked by the bridge

Deck watch officers were not familiar with the Rules of the Road and were vague as to accepted collision prevention procedure.

Most of these errors seem elementary and not likely to be made by able, intelligent officers. Yet it is just these simple mistakes that are made with discouraging frequency. It does not require genius to stand a sound, proficient deck watch, but it does take vigilance, alertness, and a highly developed sense of responsibility.

Most of the points listed above will be further discussed under separate headings farther along in the book; the others need little elaboration. The timely use of navigational lights in uncertain or dangerous maneuvering situations is proper, whether under simulated or actual battle conditions, and in any case it should be evident in these days of radar that such action could only yield incidental information to a possible nearby enemy. Running-light panels should be kept set up and bridge personnel should be drilled in switching them on quickly.

Watching the bearing of a potentially dangerous ship is an absolute essential. A steady or slowly changing bearing is dangerous—*Take action.* This means notifying the Captain if time permits, or changing course and/or stopping and backing. Even a slowly changing bearing can mean collision if the range is short.

GROUNDINGS

A second major category of emergencies is grounding. Since this subject is intimately related to the one of safe navigation, both will be discussed here. This is especially appropriate since an Officer of the Deck's major responsibility is the safe navigation of his ship while he is on watch. The other aspects of navigation are the responsibility of the ship's navigator.

Like collisions, groundings are largely attributable to human error. Here, for example, are some common errors:

Laying down ship's track too close to known shoal water
Lack of foresight in not laying down danger and turning bearings ahead of time
Excessive reliance on radar navagation alone
Failure of Officer of the Deck to notify the Captain and Navigator immediately when doubt of safe position first arises
Improper application of known gyro error
Failure to use visible navigational aids
Failure to have latest *Notice to Mariners* concerning temporary dislocation of navigational aids
Failure to use effectively a dead reckoning plot
Failure to fix position by distance run between successive bearings when only one landmark was identified
Failure to take emergency action when doubt of safe position exists
Failure to use fathometer and line of soundings.

Again, most of the errors that resulted in groundings are violations of the most rudimentary and basic principles of navigation, and again, as in collisions, the inescapable conclusion is that disaster results from carelessness and lack of a sense of responsibility rather than from a lack of knowledge. The temptation to take a chance, to slop through the watch instead of expending energy in doing the job correctly, is too often not resisted. It doesn't take a master mariner to slow, stop, change course, or notify the Captain and the Navigator that the ship's position is in doubt. Yet every year groundings occur in the Fleet that would have been just that easy to avoid.

Checking the gyro should be a constant concern of the Officer of the Deck. A range can often be used, or a sun azimuth or a bearing of Polaris can be taken. The old reliable check against the magnetic compass is required by *Navy Regulations* and should not be done in a perfunctory manner. Gyro compasses can suddenly develop large errors which can be disastrous; the only way to detect these quickly is to note the relationship, at all times, between the gyro and the magnetic compass. The quartermaster of the watch logs the readings of both in his compass record book. He should be impressed with the importance of this routine chore. After you have detected and measured a gyro error, the next important thing to do is to apply it *in the right direction.* If you do not trust your memory, refer to *Dutton,* which is available in every chart house.

RADAR NAVIGATION

"The commanding officer of a ship shall require that available electronic and other devices appropriate as aids to safe navigation be employed during periods of low visibility and at other times when needed."—*U. S. Navy Regulations, 1948* (Art. 0751).

The increasing efficiency of electronic aids to navigation presents a definite problem. There is a tendency to rely on them too completely—even to the exclusion of using such old-fashioned but useful devices as binoculars. Radar and other electronic aids should be looked upon only as important *aids* to conning a ship in low visibility. They sometimes fail or slip out of calibration or suffer directional casualties to their gyro indicators. If you must, under certain conditions, conn with your eye glued to the pilothouse PPI, be sure that your assistants are keeping an alert visual watch.

When practicable, while piloting in good visibility, use radar for training. Ask CIC for advice based on radar information, and then check against visual observations. Become familiar in good weather with typical PPI pictures; this results in confidence when you must use radar information only.

DEAD RECKONING (DR) PLOT

In the days before electronics, when good fixes were rare, hard to get, and highly valued, the DR plot was one of a navigator's most important aids. It was always run up and projected ahead. It is still just as important as it ever was. When a ship's actual position is in doubt, a DR position (modified in some cases by known factors, such as current, to give an estimated position, is the best estimate as to that position. A good navigator will have one or the other instantly available at all times. The mechanics of navigating—the furious accumulation of fixes showing where you have been—is not important. A navigator's primary duty in assuring himself of the safe navigation of his ship is to know *where the ship is going*, not where it has been. For this a DR plot is invaluable. A mechanical means of keeping this plot, the Dead Reckoning Tracer (DRT), is a sometimes neglected instrument. It should always be set up and operating when on soundings, and its setting made to conform at frequent intervals with actual fixes.

EMERGENCY ACTION

We have mentioned above the necessity for the Officer of the Deck to take action when the position of his ship is in doubt. It is difficult to imagine an Officer of the Deck so busy trying to get a cut that will put him where he thinks he is that he forgets that his ship is steaming on to disaster. But that is just what has happened. Sometimes the Captain and Navigator are not informed; often the ship needed only a slight change of course toward deep water to insure its safety. A Fleet Type Commander has stated: "The direct and final cause of most groundings is the failure of the conning officer to take the immediate emergency action of slowing, stopping, or turning to safe water when the possibility of grounding first develops. In restricted waters such possibility automatically develops with the first doubt as to the ship's position. There is no question of the advisability of taking a calculated risk in this respect during peacetime. Any risk is unacceptable under such circumstances. The realization of this one fact by Commanding Officers, Navigators, and Officers of the Deck would have prevented most of the groundings in this force."

THE NAVIGATOR AND THE OFFICER OF THE DECK

"The navigating officer shall advise the officer of the deck of a safe course to be steered and the officer of the deck shall regard such advice as sufficient authority to change the course, but he shall at once report the change to the commanding officer. In addition, the commanding officer may authorize the navigating officer, when on the bridge at sea, and provided no other officer so authorized is present, to relieve the officer of the deck in an emergency when, in the opinion of the navigating officer such action is necessary for the safety of the ship.

"The commanding officer shall be promptly informed whenever the officer of the deck is relieved in accordance with this article."—*U. S. Navy Regulations, 1948* (Arts. 1009-3 and 1009-4).

Note the language of the article concerning navigation quoted from *Navy Regulations* at the beginning of this chapter: "The Officer of the Deck shall keep himself informed." If the Navigator is on the bridge and maintaining the ship's track, it is an easy matter for the Officer of the Deck to check on the ship's position. If, however, during prolonged periods of steaming within sight of land, for example, the Navigator leaves the bridge, then the Officer of the Deck should take a more active interest in the navigation plot and must insure accurate fixes and the projection of the ship's course into safe waters. If an experienced assistant navigator is maintaining the plot then all may be well. It often happens, however, that the Navigator must depend on the Officer of the Deck or his assistant to obtain visual or radar fixes and to maintain the ship's navigational plot, particularly when well off shore but still within radar range of mountain peaks, etc. This time-honored and logical arrangement does not reduce the responsibilities of either the Navigator or the Officer of the Deck.

Navy Regulations stipulate that, except as prescribed in those regulations or as authorized by the Commanding Officer, the Officer of the Deck shall not change the prescribed course or speed of the ship unless necessary to avoid collision or imminent danger. They also state that the Navigation Officer shall advise the Officer of the Deck of a safe course to be steered, and that the Officer of the Deck shall regard such advice as sufficient authority to change the course, but that he shall at once report any such change to the Commanding Officer. These regulations further require that when in formation the Officer of the

Deck shall ensure that the assigned station is maintained. The Officer of the Deck, therefore, must make such changes of course and speed as are necessary to carry out properly the tactical orders received from higher authority, and to maintain the ship's station. When the Captain is on the bridge, the Officer of the Deck should inform him of the tactical order and the maneuver(s) contemplated. When the Captain is not on the bridge, the Officer of the Deck should immediately notify him. Except for changes of very minor effect, such as changing station when in mid-ocean, the Navigator should also be notified of any change in course or speed. This requirement to maintain assigned station gives the Officer of the Deck the authority to make the small adjustments to course and speed necessary for accurate station keeping. These adjustments are not considered changes in the prescribed course and speed.

FOG AND LOW VISIBILITY

Operating at night and in low visibility often complicates the duties of an Officer of the Deck. Radar has made possible the most complicated maneuvering and piloting under all conditions of visibility. Thus, despite the assistance of radar, the duties and responsibilities of a conning officer are in no way simplified. The fault of many inexperienced officers is that with the advent of radar, they have neglected older and more reliable means of safeguarding the ship. Radar is an *aid* against disaster, not a *guarantee.*

There is a deplorable tendency among junior officers to spend their watch with their noses glued to the PPI scope on the bridge. While continuous use must often be made of this invaluable device, it must not be done to the exclusion of visual observation and the intelligent use and appreciation of well-trained lookouts.

An Officer of the Deck must have a reasonably detailed

understanding of the capabilities and limitations of his radars. He should know exactly how to operate all the remote control radar gear, such as the PPI, on the bridge. He should know who is responsible for the maintenance of the ship's radars, and how to reach these people in a hurry. He should have the radars warmed up and checked before dark or upon the onset of fog, rain, or snow.

It is important that surface search radar equipment and DRT plotting equipment be manned while underway in reduced visibility. The Courts have held that failure on the part of a Government vessel to make use of radar while under way in low visibility was directly contributory to a collision in which the vessel was involved. Rule 29 of the *Rules of the Nautical Road,* quoted herewith, was considered applicable: "Nothing in these rules shall exonerate any vessel . . . from the consequence of any neglect to carry lights or signals, or of any neglect to keep a proper lookout, or of the neglect of any precaution which may be required by the ordinary practice of seamen, or by the special circumstance of the case."

LOOKOUTS

> "The commanding officer of a ship shall insure that lookouts are proficient in their duties, and are stationed as necessary in accordance with the best practice of seamen, having in mind any special conditions, the results to be accomplished, and the physical limitations of personnel. When under way during low visibility, or when approaching or traversing congested traffic lanes or areas, at least one lookout shall be stationed in the bow as far forward and as near the water as is feasible."—*U. S. Navy Regulations, 1948* (Art. 0751).

An important and sometimes much neglected aid to safe ship operation is the lookout. The trained human eye is still superior in many respects to the most elaborate machine. Be alert to "station additional lookouts as the circumstances require." This may be in clear weather if your ship is in much travelled sea areas. See that they have some means of rapid communication with the bridge. Be sure that they are instructed in accordance with the currently effective lookout manual. This is important to provide uniformity in reporting. See that your lookouts, as well as other personnel on duty in exposed locations, are well clothed, are rotated frequently, and are provided with an opportunity to obtain hot food and drink if low temperatures warrant it. Men cannot perform efficiently if cold, wet, or hungry; they also have a limited span of attention and cannot be expected to remain alert for long periods without a break.

Above all, let the lookout know that you are counting on his reports and consider his an important job. Be meticulous in acknowledging his reports, even if radar has already made contact. A word of praise or interest will go a long way in increasing his efficiency. Note that *Navy Regulations* require a half-hourly report on the navigational lights. "Starboard sidelight, masthead light, bright lights, sir" and "Port sidelight, range light, bright lights, sir" are the traditional reports required of the starboard and port bridge lookouts on the bell.

DARK ADAPTATION

A topic closely related to handling a ship safely at night is dark adaptation. To understand this subject you should know something about the physiology of the human eye. The cones and rods are the light-sensitive nerve endings at the back of your eye. The cones, millions of them, are concentrated in the center or bull's-eye area. The rods, more millions of them, are concentrated in a ring or circle around the cones.

You use the cones in the center of your eyes to see color

and detail and to pick up faraway objects. On the other hand, the rods, in a circle around the cones, see color only as shades of gray. They are color blind, and they see neither detail nor distant objects. You do use them, however, to see out of the corners of the eyes. Even if you can't see details, you do catch objects in motion. They won't tell you the colors in a set of signal flags, but they may keep you from running into the ship ahead.

In short, you see with the cones in daylight and with the rods at night. There is no sudden boundary. In daylight you use the cones. In full moonlight, you use cones and rods. In starlight, the cones quit work and the rods take over.

Considerable progress has been made in fitting out bridges and pilothouses with dim red lights that have a minimum effect on night vision.

It is important that only these red lights be shown, and that they not be visible from outside the ship. White lights on the deck forward, shining up from a hatch, or in the form of a carelessly used flashlight, are most detrimental to night vision and may so reduce the conning officer's perception that he may not see small craft and other objects in the water.

Red goggles are available on all ships to be worn by personnel for a half hour or so before going on watch. An additional and important aid to good night vision is the wearing of dark sun glasses during daylight if the day is bright and sunny. Recent research by doctors of Temple University Medical School has shown that exposure to bright sunlight during the day seriously interfered with night vision. Men so exposed could only see half as well at night. For the sunglasses to be effective they should be quite dark. It is recommended that officers who stand night watches wear sun glasses topside during bright days.

Since, to see at night, you are using areas of the retina which you use only slightly most of the time, you must learn a special technique for distinguishing objects. At night, objects which can be seen "out of the corner of your eye" often disappear when looked at directly. Therefore, the trick is to be sure not to stare or strain the eyes in any single direction.

A slow, roving gaze which systematically covers all quadrants of the sky or field of vision by a simple geometrical pattern picks up dimly contrasted objects. When you pick up an object this way, you naturally think of fixing your eyes upon it for a good look—and right there, you may find it disappears. You can make it reappear by using "off center" vision.

If you see a plane or ship and then lose it, don't try to bore through the darkness to find it again. Instead of staring gimlet-eyed at the spot where you lost the plane, move your eyes around the spot in a circle, focusing always slightly away from that point. If the plane or ship is there, you will pick it up again by looking to one side of it or over or under it. This takes practice, but it works.

PSYCHOLOGICAL FACTORS

(From a Pacific Fleet Letter by Fleet Admiral Chester W. Nimitz, U. S. Navy)

"There are certain psychological factors which have fully as much to do with safety at sea as any of the more strictly technical ones. A large proportion of the disasters in tactics and maneuvers comes from concentrating too much on one objective or urgency, at the cost of not being sufficiently alert for others. Thus, absorption with enemy craft already under fire has led to being torpedoed by others not looked for or not given attention; while pre-occupation with navigation, with carrying out the particular job in hand, or with avoiding some particular vessel or hazard, has resulted in collision with ships to whose presence we were temporarily oblivious. There is no rule that can cover this except the ancient one that eternal vigilance is the price of safety, no matter what the immediate distractions.

"No officer, whatever his rank and experience, should flatter himself that he is immune to the inexplicable lapses in judgment, calculation, and memory, or to the slips of the tongue in giving orders, which throughout seagoing history have so often brought disaster to men of the highest reputation and ability. Where a mistake in maneuvering or navigating can spell calamity, an officer shows rashness and conceit, rather than admirable self-confidence, in not checking his plan with someone else before starting it, *if time permits*. This is not yielding to another's judgment; it is merely making sure that one's own has not 'blown a fuse' somewhere, as the best mental and mechanical equipment in the world has sometimes done."

Chapter IX

STANDARD COMMANDS

"His (the officer of deck's) orders shall be issued in the customary phraseology of the service."—*U. S. Navy Regulations, 1948* (Art. 1005).

Nowhere in the Navy is exact phraseology as important as it is to the conning officer in giving commands to the steersman or engine-order telegraph watch. Because misunderstandings or ambiguity can be so quickly disastrous, here there must be no possibility of a mistaken meaning. There need be no confusion if only the exact and official terminology is used. Short cuts or individual variations are to be discouraged; it is important that all the enlisted men who man the ship control instruments become accustomed to receiving their commands in the same form.

MANNER OF GIVING COMMANDS

The manner in which you give commands is important. Speak clearly, loud enough to be heard, and with a positive, incisive tone. The word *helm* should not be used in any command relating to the operation of the rudder.[1]

Commands to the steersman are given in a logical sequence. The first word, "right" or "left," indicates direction and enables the steersman to start putting the wheel over at once. The second word indicates amount, as: "Right *standard* rudder." The purpose of giving the command in this manner is to insure the quick and accurate compliance of the steersman, who starts turning his wheel instantly upon hearing "right" or "left," and by the time

[1] *Helmsman* is still accepted usage, but *steersman* is to be preferred.

the amount of rudder has been specified he can bring his pointer to rest on the exact number of degrees.

Similarly, in giving commands to the engine-order telegraph (annunciator) the first term, "port (starboard) engine" or "all engines" alerts the operator and indicates which handles or knob he must prepare to move. The next part, "ahead" or "back," gives the direction of movement of the handles or knobs. The last part, "one third," "full," etc., gives the amount of the speed change and tells the engine-order telegraph operator where to stop his instrument.

The following, then, are all the commands to the engine-order telegraph: (a) "All engines, ahead one-third (two-thirds, standard, full, flank)," or "All engines back one-third, (two-thirds), (full)"; (b) "Starboard (port) engine, ahead one-third, (two-thirds), (standard), (full)"; "Port (starboard) engine, back one-third, (two-thirds), (full)."

In ships where flank speed is not otherwise provided for on the engine-order telegraph, the operator should ring up "full speed" twice.

In an emergency, when it is desired to abandon the normal accleration and/or deceleration tables and to go ahead or back with all available power as quickly as possible, the proper command is "All engines—ahead (back)—emergency." The operator should then ring up "full ahead" (or astern) three or more times in rapid succession.

The exact number of turns to be made on each engine should be indicated to the engine-room over the revolution indicator. If you desire turns other than the exact number for the speed ordered, you should specify the number of turns desired: "*Indicate* (ring up) *one one seven* revolutions." The word "revolutions" should always be included in this order to prevent any possible confusion with orders concerning course or bearings. When increasing or decreasing turns by small numbers, you should also state the exact number of turns desired; for instance "Indicate one one seven revolutions" rather than order: "Up two," or "Take off three."

When specifying turns, you should, if practicable, state the *number of turns* desired, rather than ordering turns for the *speed desired.* This may not always be practical as, for instance, when you are on the wing of the bridge, cannot see or remember the turns required, and feel that you should not leave the wing of the bridge. You should then order: *"Indicate turns for* —— knots," and require a report of the turns rung up, as well as a repetition of the command.

One-third speed and two-thirds speed are one-thirds and two-thirds of prescribed standard speed. The turns for these speeds are the number of revolutions required to make those fractions of standard speed. Full speed and flank speed are greater speeds than standard speed. They may be based on fractions of standard speed or on specified increments. The turns for these speeds are also the number of turns actually required to make them. The Officer of the Deck must bear in mind that all these speeds are speeds *through the water,* and that the revolutions to obtain them must be increased with the time the ship has been out of dock. Most ships have tables which give these data. The Officer of the Deck must know how to compute one-third, two-thirds, flank, and full speed, and their respective turns for any prescribed standard speed. When small adjustments in the speed are desired, the only command usually necessary is the one ordering the change in revolutions. However, when ordering a number of revolutions which will give a speed closer to another increment than the one already indicated, you should also ring up that nearest increment on the engine-order telegraph.

It is important that all commands be repeated back loudly and clearly by the steersman or engine order telegraph operator just as they are given by the officer at the conn. This serves as a check on the officer who originates the command and also neutralizes an inadvertent slip of the tongue such as "left" when the opposite, "right," is meant.

In addition, and just as important, the man at the wheel or engine-order telegraph must be required to report when he has complied with the command.

For example, the proper sequence would be:

(Command) "Right full rudder."

(Repeat) "Right full rudder, sir."

(When carried out) "Rudder is right full, sir."

(Command) "All engines ahead standard."

(Repeat) "All engines ahead standard, sir."

(When acknowledged by engine rooms) "All engines indicate (answer) ahead standard, sir."

It is a common practice on most ships, when maneuvering or when special sea details are manned, to have the engine-order telegraph operator wear the JV phones. By transmitting over his phones when repeating back his commands to the conning officer, the operator parallels to the engine-room all orders he is given.

If a command is given to change the speed of only one engine, then the operator, when making his final report (such as "Port engine answers ahead one third, sir"), should also inform the conning officer of the position of the other handle (such as "Starboard engine is backing full, sir"). This assists the conning officer in keeping his command to the engines in mind.

All commands to the steersman which specify a course or heading must refer to the compass by which he is steering at the time. Each course or heading is stated in three digits. For example, the order to steer 005° is: "Come right (left) to course zero zero five." If the gyro compass which the steersman is using is in error, then the actual compass course for the steersman to use should be given.

You cannot expect the steersman to perform mental arithmetic. Similarly, when steering by magnetic compass, the Officer of the Deck should apply the needed corrections and give the steerman the course which he is to maintain.

STANDARD COMMANDS TO THE STEERSMAN

Command	Meaning
"RIGHT (LEFT) RUDDER":	A command to apply right (left) rudder instantly, an indeterminate amount. Must be followed instantly by the amount of rudder desired.
"RIGHT (LEFT) STANDARD RUDDER":	Put the rudder over to the right (left) the specified number of degrees necessary for the ship to make its standard tactical diameter.
"RIGHT (LEFT) FULL RUDDER":	Put the rudder over to the right (left) the specified number of degrees necessary for the ship to make its reduced tactical diameter. The word "hard" may be used instead of "full" when maximum rudder angle is desired. This command is phrased: "Hard right (left) rudder."
"RIGHT (LEFT) FIVE (TEN, etc.) DEGREES RUDDER":	Turn wheel to right (left) until rudder is placed at the number of degrees ordered. This command is used in making changes of course. The steersman would then be ordered to steer the new course (by such command as: "Steady on course ——," in time to permit the steersman to "meet her" on the new course. The complete command would be, for example, "Right five degrees rudder. Steady on course two seven five."

Command	Meaning
"RIGHT (LEFT) HANDSOMELY":	Turn the rudder a small amount. The command is given when a very slight change of course is desired.
"GIVE HER MORE RUDDER":	Increase the rudder angle. This command is given when, with the rudder already over, it is desired to make her turn more rapidly. The command must be followed by the exact number of degrees of rudder desired.
"EASE THE RUDDER TO —— DEGREES":	Decrease the rudder angle. This command is given when the ship, turning with right (left) rudder, is turning toward or is nearing the heading desired. The command can be given, for example: "Ease to fifteen (five), etc."
"MEET HER":	Use rudder as may be necessary to check her swing. This command is given when the ship is nearing the desired course.
"STEADY," or "STEADY AS YOU GO":	Steer the course on which the ship is heading when the command is received. This command is given when, in changing course, the new course is reached or the ship is heading as desired. The steersman responds: "Steady as you go. Course ——, sir."
"RUDDER AMIDSHIPS":	Rudder angle zero. This command is given when the ship is turning, and it is desired to make her swing less rapidly.
"SHIFT THE RUDDER"	Change from right to left rudder (or vice-versa) an equal amount. This command is given, for example,

Command	**Meaning**
	when the ship loses headway and gathers sternway, to keep her turning in the same direction.
"MIND YOUR RUDDER":	A warning that the ship is swinging to the left (right) of the course because of bad steering. It is also a command to steer exactly, using less rudder.
"NOTHING TO THE LEFT (RIGHT) OF ——"	A warning to the steersman that you do not desire the ship be steered to the left (right) of the course ordered.
"HOW IS YOUR RUDDER?":	A question to the steersman. He should reply, "Five (ten) (fifteen, etc.) degrees right (left) (or) full (standard) right (left) rudder, sir."
"HOW DOES SHE HEAD?":	A question to the steersman. He should give the ship's head at the time: for example, "Two seven five, sir."
"KEEP HER SO":	A command to the steersman when he reports the ship's heading and it is desired to stead her on that heading.
"VERY WELL":	Given to the steersman, after a report by him, to let him know that you understand the situation. (Never say "All right," which is very bad sea language, and in addition may be confused with a command to the wheel.)
"COME RIGHT (LEFT) TO ——":	To put over the rudder right (left) and steady on new course ——.

In conning the ship, an officer should be governed in his supervision of his steersman by common sense and a knowledge of that steersman's capabilities. It is a common fault of inexperienced officers to give too many commands. For example, with a moderately experienced steersman, when making a change of course, it is sufficient to say: "Right standard rudder. Come to course ——." The steersman repeats the command and reports when steady on the new course.

There is usually no cause for giving all the detailed commands that are implicit in a change of course unless the steersman is a new hand or is under instruction. Similarly, in making a landing alongside, a pier, wharf, or other ship, give the steersman courses to steer—or better still, let him steer for a definite object ahead, such as a bollard, pole, or the mast of a ship.

The conning officer can err in the other direction by not giving the steersman enough information. For example, the Officer of the Deck gives the command: "Right standard rudder. Steady on course two seven zero." As the ship swings, the Officer of the Deck desires to speed up the process and says, "Increase to right full." *He must then repeat:* "Steady on two seven zero," or there is a good chance that the steersman will just leave his rudder over right full.

A final word about the steersman: Have him report properly the fact that he has been relieved and what orders he turned over to his relief. A proper report would be: "I have been relieved, sir. Steering course zero nine two, checking zero nine three."

COMMANDS TO THE LINE HANDLERS

A third major set of standard commands are those used in handling mooring lines. For going alongside, few commands are given, since heaving lines are generally used as soon as the decreasing distance permits, and the mooring lines are run across more or less automatically. Often the ship must move up the pier or wharf, and then the command is given: "Shift lines on the dock forward (or aft)," or "Walk number one forward (or aft)." Supplementary information about how far the move will be should also be sent down from the bridge.

If it is desired to use the ship's auxiliary deck machinery to haul in on a line, the command is given: "Take one (or number one) to the winch (capstan)." This may be followed by: "Heave around on one (or number one)" and then: "Avast heaving on one (or number one)."

It may be noted that the proper naval term for the line handling drum on the anchor windlass is *warping head.* Usage, however, has given authority to the synonyms *winch* or *capstan.*

Command	Meaning
"SLACK (SLACK OFF) THE BOW LINE (NUMBER 3)":	Pay out the line specified, allowing it to form an easy bight.
"TAKE A STRAIN ON ONE (or NUMBER ONE)":	Put number one line under tension.
"TAKE IN THE SLACK ON THREE (or NUMBER THREE)":	Heave in on number three line, but do not take a strain.
"EASE THREE":	Pay out number three enough to remove most of the tension.
"CHECK THREE":	Put a heavy tension on number three line but not to the breaking point, letting the line slip as necessary.
"HOLD TWO":	Take enough turns so that indicated line will not slip.
"DOUBLE UP AND SECURE":	Run additional lines or bights of lines as needed to make the mooring secure. This includes equalizing the strain on all lines, allowing slack for rise and fall of tide, etc.

Command	**Meaning**
"SINGLE UP":	Take in all lines except a single standing part to each station, preparatory to getting underway.
"STAND BY YOUR LINES":	Man the lines, ready to cast off or let go.
"LET GO":	A command to slack off smartly to permit those tending the line on the pier or other ship to cast off.
"TAKE IN ONE (or NUMBER ONE)":	Retrieve number one line after it has been cast off. When used by the conning officer, this command means to slack number one line, cast it off, and then pull it aboard. When used by the officer in charge on the forecastle, it may be preceded by the detailed commands: "Slack one" and (to the pier) "Cast off one," and means merely to retrieve number one line and bring it on deck.
"CAST OFF":	A command *to those tending the mooring lines on the pier or on another ship* to disengage or throw off the lines from over the bollards or cleats.

Chapter X

NOTES FOR THE OFFICER OF THE DECK UNDERWAY

In this chapter there will be covered a variety of subjects pertinent to the duties of the Officer of the Deck underway.

COMBAT INFORMATION CENTER (CIC)

A knowledge of the purpose, capabilities, and limitations of CIC is a requisite for every qualified Officer of the Deck. The ideal arrangement, which is achieved on many ships, is to rotate the junior officers standing deck watches between the bridge and CIC. An understanding of both stations and how they mutually support each other is important.

CIC has as its major purpose the gathering, displaying, and evaluation of data and information in order to assist the Commanding Officer in handling his ship. It also disseminates information. How well it performs the first task, that of collecting data, depends somewhat on the Officer of the Deck. The latter must appreciate his responsibility of keeping CIC informed. It cannot be a one-way process; for CIC to do its best job, it must be furnished with visual bearings and fixes, lookout reports, visual signals and messages, decisions made by the Captain or the Officer of the Deck, etc.

The capabilities of CIC are limited only by its equipment and the state of training of its personnel. A good CIC has the whole tactical picture and knows where all units are and what they are doing. It keeps track of pickets, screens, watchdogs, tomcats, CAP, SAR units, etc. In other words, CIC has the word. With this knowledge and the advantages of space, good lighting and equipment, CIC is capable of providing invaluable information and advice to the conning officer. Maneuvering problems are worked out and radar fixes are obtained which permit the CIC officer to recommend courses and speeds.

Note, however, that CIC always provides *information* and *recommendations,* not *decisions.* CIC operates like a staff officer who is always careful to *recommend* a course of action to his Admiral. Decisions are made by those responsible—and the Officer of the Deck (or the officer who has the conn) is the one responsible.

When at all practicable, the Officer of the Deck should use CIC recommendations to support his own calculations. Have a Junior Officer of the Watch work out the maneuvering board problems or get a visual fix. If necessary, do it yourself, but never permit yourself to be diverted from your most important responsibility—the safety of the ship. An Officer of the Deck who is working out a maneuvering board problem or who becomes engrossed in navigating, or who has his head down studying the PPI, cannot keep a sharp lookout ahead.

HELICOPTER OPERATIONS

Helicopters are in a state of rapid development as vital instruments of rescue and transportation. Most major naval vessels either carry and operate them or could readily be equipped to do so. An Officer of the Deck on almost any ship should know something of helicopter characteristics, capabilities, and limitations.

Weather

Officers of the Deck must know the critical wind velocities that affect helicopters. If there is no anemometer aboard the wind strength can be estimated within a few knots from the Beaufort Table that describes the appearance of the sea under different conditions of wind. The instructions for keeping the ship's log in the front of the log book include such a table. A slightly more elaborate and therefore more useful table is found in *Knight's Modern Seamanship.*

Consideration must also be given to the direction of the relative wind when maneuvering the ship to launch or receive helicopters. Battleships, cruisers, icebreakers, and other ships with considerable superstructure forward of the launching area must maneuver to obtain a relative wind near the beam in order to avoid turbulence over the landing area on the fantail. For ships that use an area forward of the ship's superstructure, such as a carrier, the relative wind should be forward of the beam.

Shipboard Procedure

The following general discussion of shipboard procedure for helicopter operations is written for the Officer of the Deck of a cruiser but should apply in all important particulars to most ship types. All Officers of the Deck should study their ship's Helicopter Launching and Recovery Bill. The material here is necessarily general and condensed.

The Officer of the Deck (under the Executive Officer) coordinates the ship's movements with the helicopter launching and recovery operations. He normally orders the helicopters to be launched and recovered, keeping the Executive Officer and the Commanding Officer informed. After obtaining permission, the Officer of the Deck may direct the helicopter struck below or brought on deck, or may change its degree of readiness.

When the helicopter is to leave the immediate vicinity of the ship the Operations Officer briefs the pilot and the Officer of the Deck in pertinent details, such as:

(a) Time of take off and time of return
(b) Mission of the flight
(c) Position and prospective movements of own ship and of other ships as pertinent at time of take-off

(d) Bearing and distance of objective at time of launching
(e) Bearing and distance of nearest land
(f) Wind and weather data as available
(g) Recognition signals and procedures
(h) Lost plane procedure
(i) Communication frequencies to be employed
(j) Magnetic variation in the operating area.

The Officer of the Deck should have a rescue boat manned when flight operations are in progress. He should also check on CIC to insure that it tracks the helicopter and maintains the required communication watch.

The Gunnery Officer or the First Lieutenant ordinarily meets all helicopters landing aboard that carry passengers, and insures that the passengers are directed to the people on board with whom they have business. Personnel from the Captain's office meet helicopters carrying guard mail and sign for all except officer messenger mail. The Officer of the Deck should anticipate mail trips and have the right people on deck to receive and sign for the mail.

Readiness

Unless conditions of readiness or emergencies dictate otherwise, the helicopter must be in all respects manned and ready, with the engine warmed up and rotors spread, ten minutes prior to the scheduled launch. The sounding of flight quarters for the helicopter may be based on this time, depending on the location and status of the plane. The senior helicopter pilot should be informed of any unscheduled flight as far in advance as possible. This will enable him to plan fuel loadings and to assemble any special gear that may be required.

Safety Precautions

The main rotor blades of a helicopter are fragile control surfaces and are treated with great care. In the event of damage to one blade the matched pair or set must be replaced, at a very high cost. An object as small as a carelessly thrown softball can damage a blade sufficiently to require the replacement of the set. The rotor blades are flexible and will bend when exposed to strong wind. Special precautions are needed to secure the blades as well as the helicopter itself, which has a higher center of gravity than conventional planes.

The rapidly rotating blades with their high tip velocity present a missile hazard of great potentialities for damage and injury to personnel. If the blades should accidentally touch a fitting or part of the ship's deck or hull while rotating, they may shatter. Accidents have occurred resulting in the loss of several lives and the wounding of many men. For this reason the number of men in the vicinity of helicopter operations must be kept at a minimum. Sightseers must keep clear. The Officer of the Deck should, as a matter of routine, have the master-at-arms clear the vicinity of all men and officers not engaged in necessary activities.

The helicopter's revolving rotors present a hazard during normal operations. Even when there appears to be sufficient clearance beneath the rotors for personnel on deck to pass or work safely, it must remembered that the blades may be deflected downward.

Downwash from the main rotor is very strong during landing and take off. All rags, hats, and other loose gear must be kept clear of the launching and landing area.

This very brief outline of helicopter shipboard operations and precautions should serve merely to introduce the subject to the Officer of the Deck. He must learn the details from publications available on board ship. The helicopter is a valuable means of rapid transportation and permits the saving of time and of lives. It, however, presents definite hazards in its operation.

THE NIGHT ORDER BOOK

"(The commanding officer of a ship) shall keep a night order book, which shall be preserved as part of the ship's official records, in which shall be entered the commanding officer's orders with respect to courses, any special precautions concerning the speed and navigation of the ship, and all other orders for the night for the officer of the deck."—*U.S. Navy Regulations, 1948* (Art. 0751).

The Officer of the Deck's major responsibility in regard to the night order book is to read it carefully, comprehend it, and comply with its directives. Initialing the night order book prior to relieving the watch signifies that the order book has been read and understood. A pitfall to be avoided is looking at the wrong page; it has happened—ships have even made a change of course directed by an Officer of the Deck who was looking at the wrong night orders.

Remember that the night order book is a permanent legal record and may at some future date be introduced as evidence before a court-martial or a court of inquiry.

SEARCH AND RESCUE (SAR)

The three Armed Services and the Coast Guard maintain jointly an almost worldwide search and rescue organization. It is effective where our Services most commonly operate, and it uses existing commands, bases, and facilities to search for and rescue personnel from air, surface, and sub-surface casualties. Certain commands, such as Commander in Chief Atlantic, are designated as SAR Coordination Centers for the purpose of coordinating the activities of ships and aircraft when an accident occurs. The senior naval officer (or one designated by him) at the scene of a disaster is known as a SAR Commander.

Previously specified radio frequencies are manned upon the occurrence of an accident, and a carefully planned procedure is followed. Detailed information giving the SAR organization and procedures, with a description of facilities at each location, is usually found in a Fleet letter or in an operation order. The SAR folder on the bridge and in CIC contains this letter as well as copies of the *Air Sea Rescue Manual* and pertinent SAR directives from current operation orders. The Officer of the Deck should be generally familiar with these directives and should know as well what radio frequencies to man in the event that an accident occurs. The word *Mayday,* when heard on any voice circuit, is an emergency call and requires that all other transmissions on that frequency cease. The Officer of the Deck should be familiar with the rescue procedures, including the special signals made by ships and aircraft when looking for survivors and when finding them.

REPLENISHMENT

Fueling, provisioning, and receiving stores, ammunition, spare parts, and personnel are all routine activities underway. They require special skills and techniques which are, by and large, not within the province of the Officer of the Deck. But certain aspects of replenishment do concern the Officer of the Deck. He should know who on board is responsible for rigging the special gear required and how long this preparation takes. He should know when to station the special details and should be familiar with the procedure, particularly the communications involved. Knowing what goes on and who does it is the important thing. Before relieving the deck when replenishment is scheduled, it is a good idea to review the ship's organization book, current effective Service Force letters, and the Naval Warfare Publication on the subject. Another source of information is the *Bureau of Ships Man-*

ual, which has a chapter devoted to the equipment used. The location of the fueling stations on various ships is usually found in the same Fleet Letter that contains masthead heights.

Fueling Methods

There are three accepted rigs for fueling at sea: the Close-in rig, the Span-wire (Elwood) rig, and the Oiler-inhaul (Elokomin) rig. The essential difference between these rigs is the method used to extend the fueling hose between vessels. In the Close-in method of fueling, the hose is extended by the use of saddles supported by lines to booms or other high locations on both vessels. In the Elwood method, the hose is supported by means of trolley blocks or pulleys which roll on a heavy span wire rigged between the two vessels. The Elwood method allows a greater separation between vessels than is possible with the Close-in rig. The increased distance permits greater speed, greater tolerance in station keeping, and greater maneuverability.

The Elokomin method is a combination of the Elwood and Close-in rigs in which the span wire is used except that the end is attached to a hose clamp instead of to the ship's structure. The outboard saddles ride on the span wire, as in the Elwood rig, but the hose is hauled across to the receiving ship by a hose messenger line attached to a winch on the tanker.

Transfer of Ammunition and Stores

To transfer ammunition and stores, three methods are in common use: the Burtoning method, the House-Fall method, and the Highline method. In the Burtoning method a line from a winch on the supply ship is led through a block or pulley on the boom of the supply ship and is connected to a similar line from a winch on the receiving ship, with a hook attached where the lines are connected. The hook catches the slings passed around the load to be transferred. The supply ship hoists the load clear of the deck, the receiving ship then heaves on its line while the supply ship pays out its line, and the load passes to the receiving ship.

The House-Fall method is a modified Burtoning rig in which the receiving ship's line, instead of being connected to a winch on the receiving ship, is passed back to the supply ship where it is connected to a second winch. The supply ship thus handles and controls both lines.

The Highline method is used for transfer of ammunition and stores and is the only method approved for transfer of personnel. In this method the highline is passed from the winch of the supply ship through a block attached to a mast or kingpost and thence to the receiving ship. A trolley block rolls on the highline and is hauled back and forth between the vessels by inhaul and outhaul lines from the block. The slings of the load are secured to a hook attached to the trolley block, the receiving ship hauls in the outhaul line while the supply ship pays out the inhaul line, and the load passes from the supply ship to the receiving ship. For transfer of personnel, a special chair is attached to the trolley block, and the highline is tended by hand instead of being led to a winch.

REFUSE DISPOSAL AT SEA

"Except as authorized by law or by regulations issued by competent authority, no oil or refuse shall be discharged into inland and coastal navigable waters." —*U.S. Navy Regulations, 1948* (Art. 1272).

"It shall be unlawful for any person to discharge . . . oil . . . into or upon the coastal navigable waters of the U.S. from any vessel . . . or suffer, or permit the discharge of oil by any method, means, or manner."—*Oil Pollution Act of 1924.*

During wartime the scattering of boxes, cans, garbage, and other trash from ships can reveal their presence to the enemy. Special precautions are found in Allied Naval Maneuvering Instructions, and additional directives may be promulgated. But during peacetime also, trash and garbage must be controlled. Seacoast communities object to the pollution of their coasts and beaches. In general, trash and garbage should not be thrown overboard underway without the permission of the Officer of the Deck. He will be guided by current directives usually found in a ship's order or in an operation order.

SPECIAL SEA DETAILS

> "The commanding officer shall insure before departure for sea that the officers and crew have been properly organized, stationed, and trained to cope effectively with any emergency that might arise in the normal course of scheduled operations."—*U.S. Navy Regulations, 1948* (Art. 0746).

While the Officer of the Deck is not responsible for the assignment of the special sea details, he is often involved in their performance of duty—particularly if it is not up to standard. Some of them, particularly the steersman, telephone talkers, and the engine-order telegraph operator, must be experienced and reliable man. Their mistakes or inattention to duty could result in serious trouble for the officer who is handling the ship, and could lead to collision or grounding. The Officer of the Deck should be aware of the importance of the special sea details and should check their stationing throughout the ship, both topside and below decks. If an unfamiliar face should turn up on the bridge, as happens occasionally even in the best organized ships, inquiry should be made at once. No man, of course, is indispensable, and changes in assignments are natural. But if a proper training program is carried out, in which the Officer of the Deck can assist, there need be no trouble in always having qualified men stationed as special sea details.

PART THREE

DUTIES OF THE OFFICER OF THE DECK NOT UNDERWAY

Chapter XI

THE WATCH IN PORT

This chapter will deal in detail with the duties of the officer of the Deck when not underway. While the immobility of his ship tends to simplify matters, it is at once apparent that other factors, such as boats, visitors, honors and ceremonies, to name only a few, make the job in port equally as demanding as the one underway.

Again it is important to emphasize the scope of the Officer of the Deck's responsibilities. From the safety of a boat miles away to the opening of a watertight storeroom door far below decks, the Officer of the Deck must feel responsible for all that goes on aboard, or is related to, his ship.

RELIEVING THE DECK

Detailed preparation is necessary before relieving the deck in port. In addition to becoming familiar with any pertinent operation plans or orders, there are usually Senior Officer Present Afloat (SOPA) instructions and port or harbor information booklets to study. These contain important local data such as services and facilities available, special hazards to boating, weather to be expected, etc. All this information is usually kept in an Officer of the Deck folder.

The following is a list of some of the most important items the Officer of the Deck must consider when relieving the deck in port. Experience or special circumstances will suggest others.

How anchored or moored
Position of ship on the chart
When anchored, the anchorage bearings and nature of holding ground

When anchored (or moored to a span), the anchor(s) in use, scope of chain, etc.

When moored to a buoy or buoys, the amount of chain and/or wire used

When moored to a pier or alongside another ship, what lines are over, and what camels, fenders, and brows are in use

When alongside, what services are being received

Tide, depth of water, amount of rise and fall of the tide, state of tide, time and direction of last swing, time of next change of tide

Status of engineering department: boilers in use, amount of steaming notice, if any; cold iron watch, if any

Anchor(s) ready for letting go

Status of gyro compass (running or secured)

State of the weather, and any anticipated changes

Other ships present, and their location

SOPA and other commanders present, and their flagships

Guardships, radio circuits manned, visual signal guards

Status of all boats—in the water, in the skids, out of commission, at the ship, away on trips, trips scheduled, etc. Status of fuel in boats

Status of aircraft

Location of Captain, Executive Officer, and any flag officer or unit commander embarked, as well as his chief of staff and staff duty officer

Time of return aboard of Captain or Executive Officer

In the absence of a flag officer or unit commander embarked, the senior officer of his staff aboard

The officers with command duty and staff duty

Work and drills in progress and scheduled

Special security measures, such as fire watches, in force

Visitors and/or workmen aboard

Important visitors expected

Liberty—the commencement and time and location of expiration. Number of men on liberty

All unexecuted orders. Status of prisoners, restricted men.

ORGANIZATION OF THE WATCH

The watch should be organized and instructed as discussed in Chapter VI (*The Watch Underway*). The administrative details, insofar as practicable, should be delegated. Each key man should be checked to insure that he knows his duties and then supervised enough to insure that he performs them. This supervision, much of which can be delegated to the Junior Officer of the Watch or the petty officer of the watch, should not be carried to extremes. To supervise means to superintend, to have the oversight and direction of. It does not mean to do the job yourself. For example, the boatswain's mate of the watch is usually charged with carrying out the day's routine. The Officer of the Deck should still check off each item at the proper time, but should do so silently and without comment unless something is overlooked. In this way the Boatswain's Mate feels that he is really responsible—a feeling he will quickly lose if an over-zealous Officer of the Deck should keep telling him: "OK, Smith, Pipe sweepers," or "You can call away the gig, now, Smith."

SECURITY

At sea there could be, under special circumstances, a more important consideration of the Officer of the Deck than the safety of his ship. One of these is the accomplishment of his mission in wartime. But in port there is little doubt that the Officer of the Deck's major responsibility is security. The safety or welfare of the ship can be threatened by many things: wind, waves, and saboteurs from outside the ship, flooding, fire, and sabotage from within the ship, for example.

EXTERNAL SECURITY

There are numerous threats to the ship's security that might arise from outside the ship. One of these is visitors of all kinds, including salesmen, agents, newsboys, and bumboats.

All strangers who approach the ship should be regarded with suspicion. We are by nature a friendly and unsuspecting people; a natural product of a secure and prosperous way of life. Therein lies a real danger, for the world beyond our own shores is rarely a friendly place. We can be certain that our enemies are always at work either trying to gain knowledge of our weapons or trying to damage or destroy them. In the past it has been all too simple for unfriendly men to come aboard as general visitors or as salesmen or agents.

Attention is invited to the following pertinent extracts from *Navy Regulations, 1948* (Art. 0733):

> "The commanding officer shall not permit foreigners or representatives of foreign activities to make inspections on board naval vessels or aircraft or at naval activities, or to inspect work being done or material assembled or stored for the Naval Establishment at private manufacturing establishments, shipyards, or other places without specific permission of the Chief of Naval Operations. When such permission has been given, he shall detail an officer to accompany the visitor, and following the inspection shall advise the Chief of Naval Operations by letter as to the details of what was shown and what was refused."

In general, dealers or tradesmen or their agents shall not be admitted within a command, except as authorized by the Commanding Officer for the following purposes:

1. To conduct public business
2. To transact specific private business with individuals at the request of the latter

3. To furnish services and supplies which are necessary and which are not otherwise, or are insufficiently, available to the personnel of the command.

There are regulations in effect in all fleets and forces restricting general and casual visiting and the approach of bumboats. The Officer of the Deck should follow these directives with great care and intelligence. Those who have a legitimate reason to come aboard must, of course, be greeted politely. But, remember that the uniform alone is not always certain assurance that a visitor is friendly. If circumstances warrant (and directives may so require), every person coming aboard should present proper identification. The more difficult the circumstances may be for the Officer of the Deck to screen visitors, the more important it is that all precautions be observed. Enemy agents may be expected to take advantage of such occasions as Armed Forces Day or the arrival of a ship at a shipyard.

In addition to identifying all individuals coming aboard (and this must not be perfunctory, even in the event of a whole shift of shipyard workmen), the Officer of the Deck should investigate all packages, parcels, boxes, etc., that are introduced into the ship. The chances are that your biggest haul will be a bottle of whiskey, but there is always the chance that materials for sabotage may be smuggled aboard.

Where sentries and armed guards are required, the Officer of the Deck will normally be required only to implement directives that are already in force. There is one important aspect of this subject, however, that should be the direct concern of the Officer of the Deck. Most enlisted men know just enough about small arms to be confident and somewhat careless in their use. The Officer of the Deck must be certain that the men assigned as sentries or guards are reasonably proficient in the use of their weapons. If doubt exists, it is always wise to send for a gunner's mate with the duty, and then hold school right there on the spot. An armed man who does not know his weapon is not only useless at his post, he is also a danger to his ship and shipmates.

In foreign ports an external security watch is usually set in accordance with a special bill in the ship's organization. This may include setting a picket boat watch around the ship.

Wind and Weather

A ship is rarely free from the danger of wind and weather. Modern ships are still vulnerable to storm damage, and today, as in the past, a Naval officer must be as good a seaman as he is a technician. The Officer of the Deck has his greatest responsibilities in relation to the weather when his ship is anchored, moored, or secured to a pier or wharf. At sea the Commanding Officer is on the bridge and makes the big decisions; in port the Officer of the Deck must often take action before the Commanding Officer can be aroused. With this in mind the problems of wind and weather presented here will be of concern mostly to the Officer of the Deck in port.

Meteorological forecasts are in general excellent but are not always available, nor can they be 100 percent accurate. They may even lull inexperienced officers into a false sense of security. The *actual* weather at your position is the important factor, not the weather that is *forecast* for your position. It is advisable for the Officer of the Deck to know what sort of weather can be expected in a certain area at a certain time of year. Pilot charts are one source of this information. There may be very little possibility of winds over 40 knots in California's San Diego Bay, for example, at any time, while in Kuluk Bay at Adak in the Aleutians the wind can whip up to 60 knots almost any afternoon. The local topography sometimes makes a great difference in the incidence of high winds that could endanger an anchored ship. Williwaws, or local, very strong gusts, are common phenomena near mountainous coasts and are not limited to the Aleutian Islands. Remember, however, that the only certain thing about weather is that it is, in the last analysis, unpredictable. When you are responsible for the safety of a ship you must always be prepared for the worst.

Scope of Chain When Anchored

It is a common rule among seamen to use a length of anchor chain equal to six times the depth of water. The following table is a more accurate guide:

Depth of Water in Fathoms	*Recommended scope (D is depth in Fathoms)*
up to 10	7 D
10 to 15	6 D
15 to 20	5 D
20 to 30	4 D
over 30 Fathoms	3 D

The above thumb rules apply only when moderately severe weather conditions are to be expected, perhaps up to force 7. In extremely high winds longer scope is necessary to take advantage of the maximum holding power of the ground tackle. See *Knight's Modern Seamanship* for a table giving maximum effective scope.

Note the much longer relative scope needed in shallow water. This is a principle often disregarded by inexperienced officers. A destroyer went aground some years ago off Block Island as a result of dragging in heavy winds. The ship was anchored in 7 fathoms with only 30 fathoms of chain. The Commanding Officer received a general court-martial.

Dragging

"When at anchor, the officer of the deck shall take proper precautions to detect and prevent dragging."
—*U.S. Navy Regulations, 1948* (Art. 1014).

The most certain indication of dragging is a change in your anchorage bearings, particularly those bearings near the beam. These should be checked at regular intervals even in good weather. Ships have been known to part their chain upon dropping the anchor, and will then, of course, drag at the slightest provocation, since only the anchor cable which is lying on the bottom is holding. Another sign of dragging anchor can be discovered by watching the chain or by feeling it on deck. Chain secured to a dragging anchor usually reveals by its pulsation that the anchor is not holding. Anchor chains pulsate or jump when the anchor is dragging because the flukes are alternately taking hold and then being pulled loose.

The Drift Lead

A drift lead should be put over the side when there is any possibility of dragging, either owing to wind, poor holding ground, or strong currents. A drift lead is a heavy lead of 30 to 50 pounds weight secured to an unmarked line. Enough hand leads to make up the needed weight may also be used if a drift lead is not available. A drift lead should be put over the side near the bow to minimize the effect on the lead of yawing. It can either be dropped straight down, with slack in the line, or dropped aft, with a taut line leading forward. In either case a change in the slackness or tautness of the line will indicate dragging, providing the ship is not yawing. As long as a ship is fairly steady, a drift lead will usually give notice in case of dragging; but if she sheers about considerably, it cannot be relied upon.

If the ship is discovered to be dragging, the Officer of the Deck should first call the Commanding Officer and then alert the engine-room and anchor detail. In a crowded anchorage or when near a lee shore, the general alarm should also be sounded. An excellent discussion of ground tackle and its use in anchoring is found in *Knight's Modern Seamanship.*

The major safeguards to prevent collision or grounding due to dragging are (1) having an anchor ready for letting go, and (2) having steam at the throttle with the steering gear ready for use and the engine-room ready to answer all bells. The latter, of course, is expensive in man hours and fuel and should not be directed without good cause. However, an Officer of the Deck should not hesitate to call the Commanding Officer and inform him of the possibility of dragging. The Commanding Officer will then decide what precautionary measures, in addition to the normal one of having a second anchor ready, shall be taken.

A ship secured to a mooring buoy by her anchor chain is rarely in danger except in exceedingly high winds, providing the mooring itself is well anchored. There are times, however, in very severe weather when destroyers and smaller vessels have been known to carry away from a mooring. This generally has happened when too little scope of chain to the buoy was used. The chop raised in the harbor by the strong winds was sufficient to cause the bow of the ship to rise and fall. Without a long enough scope of chain whose catenary provides a spring, the sudden strain as the bow of the ship pitches is sufficient to part the chain or the chain stopper on deck. To counter the yaw resulting from a longer scope to the buoy, an anchor dropped under foot is often useful.

Alongside a pier or wharf, with the standard mooring lines doubled up, there is little danger from high winds, except in extreme cases. In the event of being caught in port with a typhoon or hurricane coming, there is little to do but to make fast and hold on. The towing cable, all available spare line, and even the anchor chain may be broken out and passed ashore for added security. The Officer of the Deck, however, will rarely be in the position of having to make major decisions under these circumstances since most of his seniors will be aboard.

Extreme Temperatures

In addition to wind there may be the hazard or extreme discomfort of very low or very high temperatures. The former can cause material damage, such as ruptured fire-main risers in exposed locations, and can also greatly diminish the ship's capacity to use her armament or equipment. It is not practicable to enumerate here the many precautions and special measures to be taken when operating in extreme cold. That information is found in *The Arctic Operations Handbook* and the *Manual of Ice Seamanship.* It is merely desired to make the Officer of the Deck aware that special problems do exist.

Very high temperatures rarely affect material but they do have an important influence on the health, comfort, and efficiency of the crew. Within the limit of his prerogatives and authority the Officer of the Deck should do all in his power to help the ship's company endure the discomfort of very hot weather. In his administration of the daily routine there are many small ways in which an alert Officer of the Deck can show his appreciation of the hardships caused by extremes in temperature.

INTERNAL SECURITY

The safety of the ship may also be threatened by persons or forces within the ship. Sabotage by a member of the crew is not a pleasant subject, but it is nonetheless a distinct possibility, particularly in times of great international tension. Abrasives in lubricating oil and nails driven into multiple conductor cables are examples. Much more common, however, is the danger of fire or flooding due to factors that can be anticipated and controlled. The ship's organization specifies a security patrol and a sounding patrol. Sometimes these are combined. The Officer of the Deck should insure that these patrols are being carried out and the reports are made to him in person. In addition, the quartermaster should log the report in his notebook. The personnel involved should be instructed and supervised as necessary. In addition to routine checks for watertight closures and security, the patrols should be alert to fire hazards, such as the accumulation of trash, and the presence of combustibles, such as paint that has not been properly stowed in the paint locker.

The Officer of the Deck must also check on keys, their stowage and custody. He should be able to gain access quickly to all spaces and should check the security of key lockers and key-making machines.

Cold Iron Watch

In addition to routine security and sounding patrols, a ship whose main machinery is inactive or which has no auxiliary watch on duty below stations a "cold iron watch." These are men of the engineer force who at regular intervals inspect all machinery spaces for violations of watertight integrity and for fire hazards. The results of these inspections should be logged in the quartermaster's notebook.

Shipyard Security

> "Except in matters coming within the police regulations of the ship, the commanding officer shall exercise no control over the officers or employees of a naval shipyard or station where his ship is moored, unless with the permission of the commander of the naval shipyard or station.
>
> "The officer of the deck shall take necessary measures to prevent the introduction in or removal from the ship of unauthorized articles."—*U.S. Navy Regulations, 1948* (Arts. 0766 and 1019).

A ship under repair and overhaul in a shipyard has security problems of a particularly acute nature. All workmen coming aboard must be identified. Their tools may be stowed in racks on deck and should be safeguarded by ship's sentries. Like all other respectable working men, most shipyard workers are honest. But a small percentage will not be able to resist a souvenir or two, particularly tools that are left adrift. It must be the unpleasant duty of the watch on deck to see that theft is kept to a minimum, both by ship and shipyard personnel.

Compartments containing classified matter must be secured, either by locking or by sentries. There are sometimes occasions when yard workmen must enter these spaces, and the Officer of the Deck can anticipate matters if he keeps himself reasonably well informed of the nature and location of the work being done aboard ship. Fire watches are normally assigned each welder and burner who comes aboard. Another special precaution to be taken during shipyard work is to inspect spaces after each shift for rubbish and other material that may be fire hazards.

Other Inspections

In addition to the material inspections discussed above, the Officer of the Deck should direct his assistants, the Junior Officer of the Watch, the petty officer of the watch, or the master-at-arms to make inspections throughout the ship, day and night. These inspections are made at irregular intervals and should be as comprehensive as practicable. Their objective is the preservation of good order and discipline and the enforcement of such items of the daily routine as reveille, tattoo, and taps. By this means the Officer of the Deck keeps his finger on the ship's pulse.

SMART APPEARANCE

In port, particularly, the smart appearance of the ship, her boats, and her crew, is a major responsibility of the Officer of the Deck. There would not be space here to list all the items that must be checked to insure smart appearance. The important point is that an Officer of the Deck must first of all know what are the proper standards of cleanliness and smartness, and he must then have the courage to enforce these standards. It only takes time and a little practice to note such things as irish pennants, fouled colors, and slack halyards. But it takes energy, initiative, and patience both to observe deficiencies and take action to correct them. Junior officers vary widely in their powers of observation and in their attitude about taking action. The sooner an officer acquires a reputation for standing a taut watch and for being intolerant of anything that reflects on the good name of his ship, the more readily will the crew respond. Such an officer will not be likely to encounter men on watch on the quarter-deck in frayed or soiled uniforms. He will find that men do not try to go ashore on liberty during his watch without adequate grooming. He will, in short, find his high standards easier to maintain. On the other hand, an officer who wants above all to be popular, who has not the backbone nor the pride to stand a proper watch, will find himself in continual hot water. His superiors will be constantly breathing down his neck about the appearance of the ship, and the crew will delight in seeing how much they can get away with. Make your decision on this matter early in your career, and resolve to run a taut and efficient watch, with the ship and her personnel looking shipshape and Bristol fashion. The crew do not really admire or respect a non-regulation, easy going officer. They respect an officer who knows his job and performs his duties fairly and pleasantly but in accordance with all directives and the traditional high standards of the Navy.

Chapter XII

NOTES FOR THE OFFICER OF THE DECK NOT UNDERWAY

Of the very many different items that an Officer of the Deck in port must consider there are a few important ones that will be discussed here. It is hoped that this small elaboration of certain topics will assist officers in understanding them.

ROUTINE

An intelligently conceived and accurately implemented routine is essential to good shipboard administration. It is the Officer of the Deck's job to take care of the second part—the implementation. If the plan of the day calls for "turn to" at 1300, be sure that, as far as you can determine, the crew does "turn to" at that time. If reveille is scheduled for 0600, then see that all hands are turned out at that time. If something does not seem right about the plan of the day, consult the Executive Officer, but until he changes the routine, carry it out. The plan of the day—or morning orders, as they are sometimes called—is a directive. All hands must follow it, whether or not the word is passed over the general announcing system.

THE SIGNAL BRIDGE

An Officer of the Deck in port relies on his signal force on watch to keep him informed of ship and boat movements, particularly the approach of important officers, such as the Captain, or of important visitors. This, of course, is but one of their duties; they are usually engaged in sending or receiving visual messages. An alert signal force is one of the marks of a smart ship, and the Officer of the Deck should do all in his power to gain that distinction for his ship. He should demand a sharp lookout and prompt reports. In some large ships, such as aircraft carriers, the Officer of the Deck is not stationed where he can maintain a proper lookout himself.

RECEIVING STORES, FUEL, AND PROVISIONS

When loading stores, the Officer of the Deck makes certain that the right people have been notified and are in charge. The deck force is responsible for operating the gear and tackle needed, and the Officer of the Deck should check to see that a competent boatswain's mate is on the job. The Supply Officer or Stores Officer or his representative should check the stores aboard and direct their stowage.

Pretty much the same remarks apply to provisions. Commissary and medical personnel are required to inspect provisions from private sources for quantity and quality, and the results of these inspections are logged.

Since the Commanding Officer of the ship is responsible for both the quantity and quality of fuel oil received, it is advisable for the Officer of the Deck to take an interest in the fuel barge that comes alongside in port. The Engineer Officer (or the one with the day's duty) and the "oil king" (the petty officer in charge of fuel records) should be notified. The amount of oil received aboard is also logged, as well as the ship's drafts before and after fueling.

LIBERTY

Liberty is normally granted to the men by sections. Sections are the basic units of the ship's company. Each division is divided into three approximately equal sections (first, second, and third) for liberty, watch standing, condition watches, messing, and berthing. Each complete section is adequate to maneuver and fight the ship within the limits of the personnel available. Each section, therefore, includes adequate ratings, numbers, and qualifications to man all required stations in emergencies, including getting under way and proceeding to sea, surprise hostile action, fire and rescue, disaster ashore, etc. This is why it is important for liberty to be strictly controlled. Men frequently request special liberty, which should be granted if practicable, providing a qualified standby is on hand. But it would not do, for example, to let one of the gyro electricians go ashore if he is the only man aboard who can start the gyro and if his standby is an unqualified striker. It is always important to be generous and considerate of the men's welfare, but only when military considerations permit.

GRANTING OF ASYLUM

> "The right of asylum for political or other refugees has no foundation in international law. In countries, however, where frequent insurrections occur, and constant instability of government exists, usage sanctions the granting of asylum; but even in waters of such countries, officers should refuse all applications for asylum except when required by the interest of humanity in extreme or exceptional cases, such as the pursuit of a refugee by a mob. Officers shall neither directly nor indirectly invite refugees to accept asylum."—*U.S. Navy Regulations, 1948* (Art. 0621).

The paragraph of *Navy Regulations* quoted above is brought to the attention of the Officer of the Deck.

SHORE PATROL

> "When liberty is granted to any considerable number of persons, except in a city large enough to care properly for them without danger of disturbance or

disorder, the senior officer present shall cause to be established a sufficient patrol of officers, petty officers, and noncommissioned officers, in charge of an officer, to maintain order and suppress any unseemly conduct on the part of any member of the liberty party. The senior patrol officer shall communicate with the chief of police or other local officials and make such arrangements as may be practicable to aid the patrol in properly carrying out its duties.

"A patrol shall not be landed in any foreign port without first obtaining the consent of the proper local officials. Tact must be used in requesting this permission, and unless it is willingly and cordially given, the patrol shall not be landed. If consent cannot be obtained, the size of the liberty parties shall be held to such limits as may be necessary to render disturbances unlikely.

"Officers and men on patrol duty in a foreign country shall be unarmed; when in a United States port, officers and men shall be armed as prescribed by the senior officer present.

"No officer or man who is a member of the shore patrol shall, while on watch, on post, or at other times prescribed by the senior officer, partake of or indulge in any form of intoxicating liquor or other form of intoxicant or narcotic. The senior patrol officer shall see that the provisions of this paragraph are strictly observed, and shall promptly report to the senior officer present, in writing, all violations of it that may come to his notice. All officers and men of the patrol shall report to the senior patrol officer all violations of the provisions of this paragraph on the part of those under them."—*U.S. Navy Regulations, 1948* (Art. 0625).

"Shore patrol is established and operated in accordance with needs of the naval service for the maintenance of order, the enforcement of naval and local regulations, and the protection and assistance of naval personnel ashore.

"The jurisdiction of the shore patrol extends over all persons subject to the Uniform Code of Military Justice, both male and female.

"Shore patrol is vested with authority to discharge fully its duties and functions by the command establishing the shore patrol, and it is a principal agency through which the command enforces compliance with naval law and maintains naval discipline ashore. Officers, petty officers, and non-commissioned officers shall, by their conduct, command the respect of all members of the armed services, and reflect credit on the naval services. Members of the shore patrol are forbidden to partake of any intoxicating liquor, including beer and wine, at any time when on patrol duty or when subject to call for duty. Members of the shore patrol found to be violating the trust, or wrongfully using the authority vested in them, or found to be under the influence of intoxicating liquor or consuming intoxicating liquor while on duty will be tried by courts-martial."—*Bureau of Naval Personnel Manual, 1948.*

The material quoted above, together with the *United States Navy Shore Patrol Manual,* provides the basic directive for shore patrol activity. The Officer of the Deck in port is certain to have dealings with shore patrol personnel, if only to see that the men and officers detailed from the ship are sent ashore. It is desirable that the Officer of the Deck know in general how the shore patrol is organized, what its purpose is, and how it operates. Normally, ship's personnel detailed for shore patrol duty will already have been instructed in their duties and responsibilities. It is a function of the Executive Officer to insure that a division officer or experienced petty officer does the instructing. But on occasion an Officer of the Deck may have to detail men who have not been instructed. It is his responsibility, then, to break out the manual and see that the men are informed.

Requirements for shore patrol are generally included in *SOPA Instructions.*

APPREHENSION AND RESTRAINT

An Officer of the Deck must know the difference between *apprehension* and the three degrees of *restraint.*

The Officer of the Deck will have occasion to receive custody of men charged with misconduct. The men may be delivered by the Shore Patrol or by an officer or petty officer aboard ship. They may even deliver themselves for minor offenses, such as being out of uniform. It is important that the Officer of the Deck know the legal meanings of the terms involved, and also know what action to take.

All officers, petty officers, and non-commissioned officers of any service have authority to apprehend offenders subject to the Uniform Code of Military Justice. Other enlisted men may do so when assigned shore patrol, military police, and similar duties. *Apprehension* is accomplished by clearly informing the person that he is being taken into custody. He should be told at the same time what he is accused of. It should be noted here that *apprehension,* in the Armed Services, has the same meaning as *arrest* has in civilian life. Just as a police officer informs a citizen that he is under *arrest* so does a naval officer tell a man that he is being apprehended or is being taken into *custody*. *Custody* is temporary control over the person apprehended until he is delivered to the proper authority (on board ship, the Officer of the Deck). In general, persons who have authority to apprehend may exercize only such force as is actually necessary. Petty officers should apprehend officers only under very unusual circumstances, such as to avoid disgrace to the Service or to prevent the escape of a criminal.

Restraint as a general term involves some degree of deprivation of free movement of the person restrained. There are three degrees of restraint: *confinement, arrest,* and *restriction in lieu of arrest.* Restraint is never imposed as a punishment, and the degree of restraint used should be no more severe than that necessary to insure the presence of the offender at further proceedings in his case. Thus, even though a man has committed an offense or is suspected of such, he need not be restrained to any degree if his presence is assured at future proceedings.

Only the Commanding Officer may impose any degree of restraint on a commissioned officer or a warrant officer. If it is desired to restrain an officer, the Commanding Officer must be notified.

Only officers may ordinarily impose any degree of restraint on an enlisted man. However, the Commanding Officer may delegate this authority to warrant officers and enlisted men.

Confinement is an actual physical restraint imposed in serious offenses to insure the presence of the person.

Arrest is the moral restraint of a person, by an order, oral or written, to certain specified limits pending disposition of charges against him. It is not imposed as punishment. It is imposed only for probable cause, based on known or reported facts concerning an alleged offense. *Arrest* relieves a man of all military duties other than normal cleaning and policing. *Arrest* is imposed by telling a man (or officer) of the limits of his arrest.

One of the disadvantages of placing an accused in arrest is that he may no longer be required to perform his military duties, and if the authority ordering this type of restraint requires the accused to perform his military duties, the arrest is automatically terminated. Consequently, a lesser form of restraint is allowed. This is called: "Restriction in lieu of arrest."

Restriction is a restraint of the same nature as arrest, imposed under similar circumstances and by the same authorities, but it does not involve the suspension of military duties.

A prisoner at large (PAL) is a man under arrest or restriction and it is important that he be informed of which status is applicable in his case.

Persons apprehended aboard ship are delivered to the custody of the Officer of the Deck together with a misconduct report. The Officer of the Deck informs the Executive Officer (or Command Duty Officer) and receives instructions as to the nature of restraint to be imposed on the man. This, of course, normally depends on the gravity of the offense. Assuming that formal restraint, such as arrest, is ordered, the Officer of the Deck notifies the offender, insuring that he, the offender, understands the nature of his restraint and the penalties for violation of restraint. The Officer of the Deck secures the offender's written acknowledgement of his notification by his signature upon the misconduct report slip, and then turns the offender over to the master-at-arms. The whole matter is logged, of course, with full details.

Restraint does not have to be imposed on an accused. The whole purpose of restraint is to insure the presence of the accused at a subsequent trial or disposition of his case. Thus, if the offense is relatively minor, and it can be assumed that the accused will not attempt to leave the area to avoid trial, no restraint is necessary. Confinement is used before trial only in such cases where there is a risk of the accused attempting to escape punishment. The lesser forms of restraint impose a burden on the accused because it is a punishable offense to violate the limits of the restraint. Restraint once imposed may not be removed except in the following circumstances:

Arrest and Restriction in lieu of Arrest may be lifted by the authority ordering the restraint, or a superior in his chain of command. Once a person is confined, he passes from the jurisdiction of the person ordering confinement, and can only be released by order of the Commanding Officer of the activity where the confinement takes place. On board ship, this poses no special problem because generally, the authority ordering the confinement is also the commanding officer of the confining activity.

RECEPTION AND DETACHMENT OF PERSONNEL

An Officer of the Deck will appreciate that the first impression made on newly reporting officers and men is important. For this reason certain fixed procedures should be carried out. The Officer of the Deck should establish the officer's identity, should make appropriate arrangements for his baggage, and then see that the officer is escorted to the Executive Officer or the Command Duty Officer. An enlisted man, after identification and assistance with baggage, should be turned over with his records to the Chief (or duty) Master-at-Arms who takes him below to the ship's personnel office. After the necessary paperwork is completed in the personnel office, the Master-at-Arms should assign the man a bunk and locker. This all sounds simple, but a large draft of new men received just before sailing will often present real problems. Whatever the means you employ, try to insure that both men and officers are made to feel welcome and are processed aboard as quickly and painlessly as practicable.

PART FOUR

MISCELLANEOUS

Chapter XIII

BOATS

"When embarked in a boat the senior line officer (including commissioned warrant and warrant officers) eligible for command at sea, has authority over all persons embarked therein, and is responsible under all circumstances for the safety and management of the boat."—*U.S. Naval Regulations, 1948* (Art. 1331).

"Boats shall be regarded in all matters concerning the rights, privileges, and comity of nations as part of the ship or aircraft to which they belong.

"In ports where war or insurrection exists or threatens, the commanding officer shall:

"(a) Require that boats away from the ship or aircraft have some appropriate and competent person in charge.

"(b) See that steps are taken to make their national character evident at all times."—*U.S. Navy Regulations, 1948* (Art. 0757).

"The officer of the deck shall insure that the ship's boats are properly manned and equipped and are not loaded beyond their safe capacity, consistent with weather conditions. He shall see that the required safety appliances are in place and in good order, and that the crews understand their use and observe all prescribed safety precautions.

"He shall inform himself of all boats or other craft that come alongside or leave the ship, and shall permit them to lie at the gangway no longer than necessary. He shall promptly notify the officers concerned when stores or other materials or services arrive which require their knowledge or action.

"He shall insure that the ship's boats and their crews present at all times a creditable appearance, that the boats are handled smartly, and that the crews observe the rules for preventing collisions and the regulations pertaining to honors and ceremonies.

"He shall insure that boats are properly secured when not in use.

"Boats and aircraft within sight of the ship shall be watched in order that aid may be sent promptly if needed."—*U.S. Navy Regulations, 1948* (Art. 1016).

In the "Old Navy," boats were vital appendages of ships. Units of the Fleet usually anchored in port instead of mooring to a wharf or pier as is often the practice now. Ship's boats were the sole contact with the beach, and their appearance and the seamanship of their crews were a major factor in judging the Service reputation of their parent ships. Officers took intense pride in the smartness of their boats and their interest was reflected in the attention of petty officers and non-rated men in caring for and operating their boats.

World War II marked the removal of many ship's boats and introduced the use of shore-based boat pools for most purposes if a ship was not alongside a pier or wharf. The resultant loss of skill in boat seamanship by both men and junior officers has been a post-war problem that is only gradually being solved. Several serious and many minor boat accidents have occurred which not only have resulted in a tragic loss of life, but have been a reflection upon the efficiency and the seamanship of the Navy.

With this brief introduction the Officer of the Deck can readily see that the handling of his ship's boats presents a grave responsibility as well as a challenge to his foresight, seamanship, and pride. Close and informed supervision is necessary, not only to maintain the efficiency of highly important boat service, but also to insure the safety of personnel.

AT SEA

> "In port he (the officer of the deck) shall require the coxswains of the lifeboats to inspect and report to him daily at sunset the condition of their boats as to readiness for service; and at sea he shall require a like inspection and report at the beginning of each watch."—*U.S. Navy Regulations, 1948* (Art. 1013).

At sea the Officer of the Deck has relatively simple duties pertaining to ship's boats. Unless a boat is launched while the ship is underway, he is only concerned with the readiness of the lifeboats. This can best be assured by questioning the coxswains when they make their required report. Learn, if you do not already know it, the coxswain's own qualifications as well as those of his crew. Know where they are stationed and how long it takes to alert them. Know also who the men are who will lower the boat in an emergency and how long this process will take, as well as who is ordinarily in charge of the lowering. The boatswain's mate of the watch is your principal assistant for boats.

The readiness of the boat engine, the amount of fuel in the boat, and the special rescue equipment carried are other matters of interest to the Officer of the Deck. In cold weather, special precautions must be taken to keep the engine warm, either by frequent startings or by heaters. It should go without saying that all ship's boats at sea should be full of fuel. Special equipment will vary with different ships and their employment, but it is always a good idea for the Officer of the Deck to check the lifeboat's equipment once each watch. Have the coxswain make an inventory and report; he is always responsible for the condition as well as the appearance of his boat and crew.

All these matters are a part of the routine of a well run ship, but the Officer of the Deck can never be complacent and assume that all is well, when, by asking a few questions, he can *make sure*. For if a lifeboat is ever needed and is not ready, or is launched with a green crew or short of fuel or gear, the Officer of the Deck is certain to be held at fault.

IN PORT

Boats present a major responsibility to the Officer of the Deck in port in their operation, appearance, and security.

Calling away, dispatching, fueling, and receiving boats can be a complicated and most harassing business for the Officer of the Deck who has not organized his watch to handle it. Some sort of status board or sheet is almost mandatory to keep track of a number of boats on a variety of missions. Assuming that you have an assistant maintaining a record of boat employment and conditions of readiness, there is still necessary an intelligent and personal supervision by the Officer of the Deck. Boats should be inspected for appearance from the quarter-deck, their equipment should be checked and the coxswain instructed. If the instructions are complicated, send for the coxswain and discuss the matter. If you have any misgivings about his memory, put your instructions in writing. Make your orders short, complete, and reasonable. Never send in a boat to wait for someone without putting a time limit on the trip. Otherwise, if the passenger or passengers fail to show up, you have lost the services of a boat until you can get word to the beach. That might take hours. Boat's crews are sometimes kept up long hours for no good reason because of some unforeseen change of plans ashore. The proper procedure for all boats, except, of course, a gig or a barge, is to direct them to wait for someone only for a certain time or until a specified hour.

SCHEDULES

Boat schedules are normally prescribed by the Executive Officer and should be followed meticulously by the Officer of the Deck. Only the most unusual circumstances should cause a cancellation of a scheduled boat, particularly at night when there may be people ashore who are planning to return to the ship in that boat. If a scheduled boat trip must be canceled, get permission from the Executive Officer or duty head of department, and then pass the word.

It is quite common to have men and officers waiting to leave the ship who have the same destination as the gig or the barge. The Officer of the Deck should make every effort to learn the policy or practice of the senior officer concerned, and, if permissible, embark the people before the Captain or Admiral comes onto the quarter-deck. If doubt exists, it is quite appropriate to ask the senior officer if he desires to take any officers and/or men to his destination. If the answer is affirmative, as is invariably the case, make every effort to expedite loading the boat. There are officers in every ship who do not seem to know that juniors always enter boats (and vehicles) *first* and leave them *last*.

EQUIPMENT

Boat compasses, life jackets, and other items of boat equipment must be checked by the Officer of the Deck as circumstances warrant. For long boat trips or when low visibility is likely, the boat compasses should be observed during the first trip in any port or anchorage, with headings and time on each course recorded in the boat's compass book. This practice will make boating much safer and more certain later on. Life jackets, foul weather clothing, harbor charts, and fire fighting equipment are other items of boat equipment in which the Officer of the Deck should take a personal interest. Life jackets should be checked and their use directed when weather or sea conditions so indicate. The number of personnel allowed in a boat should not exceed the number of life jackets in that boat. Do not assume that boats belonging to other units, such as boat pools, are properly equipped; have them inspected if they are to be used by your ship.

CAPACITY

The capacity of Navy boats is indicated on the boat label plate secured in the boat when it was built. This is maximum capacity and should always be reduced in rough weather or when stores or other cargo are carried at the same time as passengers.

INSPECTION

The Engineer Officer designates a junior officer or a particularly well qualified petty officer to inspect boat machinery daily. In addition, the First Lieutenant makes periodic checks on the equipment carried in each boat and the condition of the boat itself. While these inspections can be assumed to be complete, they do not relieve the Officer of the Deck of exercising the prudence and foresight expected of a good seaman. The appearance and smartness of ship's boats always require additional attention on the part of the Officer of the Deck. When there is a question of safety or security, such as life jackets in a boat, there is similarly, the need for personal supervision by the Officer of the Deck. He should not assume that routine inspections are enough to guarantee that certain equipment will be in a certain boat at a particular time.

APPEARANCE

The subject of the appearance and smartness of a ship's boat has been mentioned before in this book. It is one that will always be prominent among officers who take pride in their ship and in their Service. A smart boat reflects a smart ship and is often the means by which a ship and her crew are evaluated. Not only do fresh and neat paintwork and fancy knotwork make a good impression, but even more important is the manner in which the boat is handled. The skill and good sea manners of the coxswain are always noted.

The Officer of the Deck can be a major factor in maintaining high standards in the ship's boats. His critical appraisal of crew and boat as it comes alongside is the first step. If he then corrects any deficiencies possible (or submits a memorandum to the Executive Officer if he cannot), he has done a great deal to insure that his ship will be well represented by the boats that are employed during his watch.

SECURITY

One method to insure the safe and efficient operation of a boat is to provide a boat officer. This is only true, of course, when the officer assigned is qualified. An ensign fresh from Officer Candidate School, with no previous seagoing experience, would be of little value. A boat officer should be assigned:

(1) In foul weather, fog or high winds, existing or forecast

(2) For first boat trips in foreign or unfamiliar harbors

(3) For the return of large liberty parties, particularly late at night just before sailing.

A boat officer should wear a web belt and, except where prohibited by competent authority, a pistol as a badge of authority which distinguishes him from officer passengers. In cases where there are insufficient commissioned or warrant officers, it is customary to assign deck rating chief petty officers as boat officers.

DISCIPLINE IN A LIBERTY BOAT

A familiar problem in handling liberty parties is the maintenance of good order and discipline, especially just before sailing for the forward area. High spirits and an uninhibited display of "smokestacking" and salty language are to be expected. When matters pass the bounds of decency or when they threaten the comfort and safety of the more reserved members of the liberty party the boat officer or the senior officer aboard must maintain order. There is a correct and fairly easy way to do this, and also a wrong and sometimes disastrous method. The officer in charge should detail a number of petty officers, as many as circumstances require, to preserve order. The petty officers usually do this by separating the most exuberant of the troublesome men and persuading them to sit down and be quiet. The wrong method is for the officer in charge to attempt to deal with the noisy men directly. This could lead to disrespectful language or conduct and may even result in violence to the person of the officer who is trying to do the job singlehanded. It is important to note here the obligation that an officer has of avoiding, if possible, a situation involving a serious offense by an enlisted man. A hasty blow by a man befuddled by drink could wreck his career.

It should be noted that in a boat the senior line officer eligible for command at sea is the responsible officer. It has happened that an officer did not realize that he was responsible until after an accident had occurred. In an emergency, of course, you have little time to stop and compare signal numbers with fellow officer passengers; the thing to do, if you believe the boat is in danger, is to act quickly and decide the matter of seniority later. With a boat officer on duty there is normally no reason for a senior passenger to interfere unless he believes a dangerous situation is developing which is beyond the capacity of the boat officer to handle. In this extremity, the senior line officer passenger (eligible for command at sea) should take charge. If he does take over he should do so decisively, informing the crew and the boat officer of his action. This action should only be taken in case of an emergency, since the boat officer has presumably been assigned his responsibility by competent authority.

BOAT CREWS

The Officer of the Deck may have little to do with the training of boat crews, but he must make certain that those operating boats during his watch are qualified. Sometimes on a late boat trip a new man will appear as engineer, bow hook, or even as coxswain. Allow these men to go along for instruction if they wish to, but never as a substitute for a qualified crew member. It has even happened that after receiving his instructions from the Officer of the Deck the coxswain has delegated his job to an unqualified seaman. This sort of an incident contributed to the swamping of a liberty boat a few years ago that caused the loss of 18 lives. The point here is that the Officer of the Deck must know his boat crews and must be particularly alert to the qualifications of the coxswains.

A final aspect of boat security is that of securing the boat when not in use. The safest procedure to follow, when practicable, is to hoist boats in at night or in bad weather. If this cannot be done, the boats when hauled out to the boom should be under surveillance. Never permit boats to lie at the accommodation ladder unattended. Boats usually ride well at the boom; it is the practice of making fast astern that is risky in bad weather. Boat lines chafe through easily, and boat keepers or boat sentries are normally employed in bad weather if there is any doubt about the security of the ship's boats.

BOAT ORDERS

When giving orders to the coxswain of a boat, do so in an explicit and seamanlike manner. Do not say for example, "All right, coxswain, shove off and get the Navigator at the Dock Street Landing." Instead, say: "Coxswain! When told to shove off, go to the Dock Street Landing and bring off the Navigator, Lieutenant Commander Jones. If he does not show up by ——— o'clock return to the ship. Do you understand?" When he answers in the affirmative, say: "Shove off and carry out your orders." Remember that a boat "hauls out" to the boom, it does not "tie up" or "secure" to the boom. A ship "makes fast" to a pier, while a boat may "make fast" to the accommodation ladder (not the gangway). A boat may be "secured," but this means a more permanent fastening than to "make fast." The expression "tie up" is not a proper naval term and should be avoided.

There is a technique in properly loading a large liberty boat that is worth learning. It is one of those small but significant marks of an efficient Officer of the Deck and a smartly run ship. After the chief petty officers have been embarked, the other men should be required to go forward in the boat and load from forward aft. It may take a little supervision to prevent men from filling up the center section first, but it will prevent people climbing over each other, or the dangerous practice of men walking along the gunwales.

Chapter XIV

HONORS AND CEREMONIES

"The officer of the deck shall see that all regulations concerning salutes, honors, and ceremonies, except as modified by orders of competent authority, are carefully observed."—*U.S. Navy Regulations, 1948* (Art. 1018).

"The honors and ceremonies prescribed in these regulations may be dispensed with when directed by the Secretary of the Navy, or when requested by an individual to whom such honors and ceremonies are due."—*U.S. Navy Regulations, 1948* (Art. 2101).

"No salute shall be fired in honor of any nation or any official of any nation not formally recognized by the Government of the United States; and, except as authorized by the Secretary of the Navy, no other honors or ceremonies prescribed in these regulations shall be rendered or exchanged with such nations or officials."—*U.S. Navy Regulations, 1948* (Art. 2102).

"Should the required number or frequency of international salutes, official visits, or other honors and ceremonies be deemed excessive, the senior officer present in the United States naval service may make, subject to the requirements of international courtesy, such modification as circumstances warrant and as may be agreed upon with the responsible officials or the senior officer present of the nation involved."—*U.S. Naval Regulatons, 1948* (Art. 2103).

Honors and ceremonies are based on a long established code of customs, agreements, and regulations, which, in general, is common to all navies. With some important exceptions, these honors and ceromonies occur in port, and the manner in which they are rendered or carried out under your supervision as Officer of the Deck does much to make the reputation of your ship for smartness. Because of the frequent international character of honors and ceremonies, it is especially important that they be so rendered and conducted as to reflect credit on the Navy and on the United States.

Honors and ceremonies may vary from two side boys for an ensign to an official visit of the President or head of a foreign state. It is well, in your own mind, to divide honors into two classes: those which you must know on the instant without looking them up, and those which you will normally have time to look up and which should not be trusted to memory. Most ships keep a "table of honors" posted on the quarter-deck.

The question of whether or not to fire a salute will generally be decided by the Captain, but the firing of the salute, as, in fact, the execution of all honors and ceremonies, will be in your hands as Officer of the Deck to initiate.

This chapter will contain pertinent extracts from Chapter 21, *U.S. Navy Regulations, 1948*. Enough will be reproduced herein to enable the Officer of the Deck under normal conditions to discharge his duties. On special occasions, such as the death of an important person, it will be necessary to refer to *Navy Regulations* itself. The extracts reproduced here will enable the Officer of the Deck to have all the guidance he will need under ordinary circumstances without the necessity for breaking out a larger and heavier volume. As an added convenience, certain tabular data are concentrated on a sheet folded at the end of this chapter.

With honors and ceremonies, as with nearly all your activities as Officer of the Deck, it is important to look ahead. Generally speaking, you should be able to estimate quite accurately the degree of readiness required under existing conditions. If anchored in bad weather at an advanced base, with air attack possible, you would not be likely to need side boys standing by. On another occasion it might be necessary to have the full guard ready at a moment's notice.

THE IMPORTANCE OF BEING INFORMED

The most important assistance an Officer of the Deck requires in rendering honors is adequate advance notice. While you have to be prepared, under normal circumstances, to discharge your duties with little or no notice, it is important to impress upon your signal force and the other personnel on watch the necessity for vigilance. All boats flying colors or pennants should be watched carefully. Sometimes they may appear to be headed clear, and then suddenly come alongside. It is not difficult to imagine the embarrassment that will be suffered by everyone from the Captain on down if a VIP ("Very Important Person") comes aboard unobserved.

THE QUARTER-DECK

> "The commanding officer of a ship shall establish the limits of the quarter-deck and the restrictions as to its use. The quarter-deck shall embrace so much of the main or other appropriate deck as may be necessary for the proper conduct of official and ceremonial functions."—*U.S. Navy Regulations, 1948* (Art. 2160).

The quarter-deck is that part of the ship so designated by the Commanding Officer. It is normally on the main deck near the gangways. It is marked off by appropriate lines, deck markings, decorative cartridge cases, or fancy work, and is always kept particularly clean and shipshape. *Men not on duty should not be allowed on or near the quarter-deck.* The dignity and appearance of the quarter-deck are a symbol of the quality of a ship and her crew. Be zealous in upholding both this dignity and appearance, together with the highest standards of smartness on the part of your personnel.

Tending the Side

> "The officer of the deck shall see that all persons coming aboard or alongside the ship are courteously treated.
>
> "Unless prevented by urgent duty, he shall be at the gangway to receive, and shall accompany to the side, all officers or distinguished visitors. When so prevented, he shall send a junior officer of the watch to represent him.
>
> "Except for those persons over whom he has no authority, he shall require all persons leaving or returning to the ship to report to him or his representative; on leaving the ship they shall report authority to do so."—*U.S. Navy Regulations, 1948* (Art. 1017).

Gangways should always be tended smartly by the Officer of the Deck or one of his assistants. It may be well to note here that a gangway is an opening in the bulwarks or rail giving access to the ship (quarter-deck). The term should not be confused with accommodation ladder. For reasons of both security and courtesy, every person coming aboard should be greeted by a member of the watch immediately, his business and/or credentials ascertained or examined, and appropriate steps taken to escort him below or else to send for the person he wishes to see. Officers' guests should be shown to the wardroom. It is considered a great mark of slackness and unseamanlike organization for someone to get on board without having been met properly.

When an officer comes aboard, his boat will normally lie alongside the accommodation ladder until it receives its orders. The Officer of the Deck should ask the visitor or his aide what orders are desired for his boat (gig) (barge).

Side Boys

Side boys are the first men to come under the surveillance of an important personage or visitor, and for this reason they should always be particularly smart, with shoes well polished, and with uniforms clean or brushed off. They should be kept together under the eye of a petty officer and not employed in any activity that will spoil their good appearance or cause them to be absent from the quarter-deck. See that they are properly instructed and are able to fall in properly without undue confusion. Similar precautions should be taken with the guard and band as are taken with side boys.

Piping the Side

The call "alongside" is sounded so as to finish just as the visitor's boat makes the accommodation ladder. During this pipe the side boys and the boatswain's mate stand at attention but do not salute.

The call "over the side" starts just as the visitor's head appears at quarter-deck level. When visitors approach over a brow, a corresponding point at the outboard end of the brow should be selected. Side boys and boatswain's mate salute on the first note, and drop their hands from salute on the last note. The boatswain's mate may salute with his left hand. Saluting and piping procedure is reversed when a visitor leaves.

CHECK-OFF LIST FOR THE OFFICER OF THE DECK

Upon notification of an official visit, the Officer of the Deck should:

(a) Check proper table of honors.

(b) Notify Admiral, Chief of Staff, Commanding Officer, Executive Officer, Command Duty Officer, Navigator, Senior Watch Officer, Flag Lieutenant, C.O. Marine Detachment.
(c) Have on deck a qualified bugler, a qualified boatswain's mate and a quartermaster.
(d) Inspect and rehearse side boys.
(e) Inspect quarterdeck for appearance.
(f) Station alert lookout, notify signal bridge to be alert and have personal flag ready.
(g) Notify band.
(h) Notify gunnery officer if a salute is required.

Chapter 9, *Shipboard Procedures*, NWP 50, contains detailed honors and ceremony procedures.

EXTRACTS FROM NAVY REGULATIONS

The following quotations are inserted as a matter of convenience to the Officer of the Deck. Articles of special or limited application have been omitted and are so indicated. See also Chapter 9 in *Shipboard Procedures*.

Section 1—General

Arts. 2101, 2102 and 2103 are quoted at the beginning of this chapter.

Section 2—Morning and Evening Colors, Salutes to the National Ensign

Arts. 2105, 2106 concerning the playing of the National Anthem are omitted.

2107. Morning and Evening Colors.

1. The ceremonial hoisting and lowering of the national ensign at 0800 and sunset at a naval command ashore or aboard a ship of the Navy not underway shall be known as Morning Colors and Evening Colors, respectively, and shall be carried out as prescribed in this article.

2. The guard of the day and the band shall be paraded in the vicinity of the point of hoist of the ensign.

3. "Attention" shall be sounded, followed by the playing of the national anthem by the band.

4. At Morning Colors, the ensign shall be started up at the beginning of the music and hoisted smartly to the peak or truck. At Evening Colors, the ensign shall be started from the peak or truck at the beginning of the music and the lowering so regulated as to be completed at the last note.

5. At the completion of the music, "Carry On" shall be sounded.

6. In the absence of a band, "To the Colors" shall be played by the bugle at Morning Colors, and "Retreat" at Evening Colors, and the salute shall be rendered as prescribed for the national anthem.

7. In the absence of music, "Attention" and "Carry On" shall be the signals for rendering and terminating the salute.

8. During colors, a boat underway within sight or hearing of the ceremony shall lie to, or shall proceed at the slowest safe speed. The boat officer, or in his absence the coxswain, shall stand and salute except when dangerous to do so. Other persons in the boat shall remain seated or standing and shall not salute.

9. During colors, vehicles within sight or hearing of the ceremony shall be stopped. Persons riding in a passenger car or on a motorcycle shall remain seated at attention. Occupants of other types of military vehicles remain seated at attention in the vehicle; the individual in charge of each such vehicle (other than the driver) shall get out of the vehicle and render the hand salute.

10. After Morning Colors, if foreign warships are present, the national anthem of each nation so represented shall be played in the order in which a gun salute would be fired to, or exchanged with, the senior official or officer

present of each such nation; provided that, when in a foreign port, the national anthem of the port shall be played immediately after Morning Colors, followed by the national anthems of other foreign nations represented.

2108. Salutes to the National Ensign.

1. Each person in the naval service, upon coming on board a ship of the Navy, shall salute the national ensign if it is flying. He shall stop on reaching the upper platform of the accommodation ladder, or the shipboard end of the brow, face the national ensign, and render the salute, after which he shall salute the officer of the deck. On leaving the ship, he shall render the salutes in inverse order. The officer of the deck shall return both salutes in each case.

2. When passed by or passing the national ensign being carried, uncased, in a military formation, all persons in the naval service shall salute. Persons in vehicles or boats shall follow the procedure prescribed for such persons during colors.

3. The salutes prescribed in this article shall also be rendered to foreign national ensigns and aboard foreign men-of-war.

Section 3—Hand Salutes and Other Marks of Respect (omitted)

Section 4—Gun Salutes

2114. Saluting Ships and Stations.

Saluting ships and stations of the naval service are those designated as such by the Secretary of the Navy or his duly authorized representative. The gun salutes prescribed in these regulations shall be fired by such ships and stations. Other ships and stations shall not fire gun salutes, unless directed to do so by the senior officer present on exceptional occasions when courtesy requires.

2115. Gun Salutes to the Flag of the President or the Secretary of State (omitted).

2116. Gun Salutes to the Flag of the Secretary of Defense, the Deputy Secretary of Defense, the Secretary of the Navy, an Assistant Secretary of Defense, the Under Secretary or an Assistant Secretary of the Navy (omitted).

2117. Gun Salute to a Foreign Nation (omitted).

2118. Returning Salute to the Nation fired by Foreign Warship (omitted).

2119. Gun Salutes to the Flag of a Foreign President, Sovereign, or Member of a Reigning Royal Family (omitted).

2120. Gun Salutes when Several Heads of State are Present (omitted).

2121. Authority to Fire Gun Salutes to Officers in the United States Naval Service.

Gun salutes prescribed in these regulations for officers and officials entitled to 17 or more guns shall be fired on the occasion of each official visit of the individual concerned. Gun salutes prescribed in these regulations for officers and officials entitled to 15 guns or less shall not be fired unless so ordered by the senior officer present or higher authority.

2122. Gun Salutes to the Senior Officer Present.

1. A flag officer who is the senior officer present shall be saluted by the senior of one or more ships arriving in port.

2. When a flag officer embarked in a ship of his command arrives in port, and is the senior officer present, or when a flag officer assumes command and becomes the senior officer present, he shall be saluted by the former senior officer present.

3. A gun salute shall be fired by his flagship when a flag officer who is the senior officer present assumes or is relieved of command, or is advanced in grade.

4. When a flag officer who is not the senior officer present assumes command, he shall fire a salute to the senior officer present.

5. The provisions of this article shall be subject to the provisions of article 2128.4 and shall apply, where appropriate, to officers of the naval service in command ashore.

2123. Gun Salutes to Foreign Flag Officers.

1. When a ship enters a port where there is present no officer of the naval service senior to the senior arriving officer, and finds displayed there, afloat or ashore, the flags of foreign flag officers of one or more nations, salutes shall be exchanged with the senior flag officer present of each nation.

2. The senior officer present of the United States Navy in a port shall exchange gun salutes with the senior foreign flag officer displaying his flag in an arriving warship, provided such flag officer is the senior officer present of his nation.

3. Upon departure from port of the senior officer present of the United States Navy, his successor shall exchange gun salutes with the senior flag officer present of each foreign nation.

4. The senior officer present of the United States Navy shall exchange gun salutes with the senior officer present of a foreign nation when either hoists the flag of an increased grade.

5. In firing the salutes prescribed by this article, the following rules shall govern:

(*a*) An officer of a junior grade shall fire the first salute.

(*b*) When officers are of the same grade, the arriving officer shall fire the first salute.

(*c*) Seniors shall be saluted in order of rank except that when firing salutes to two or more foreign officers of the same grade, the first salute fired to an officer in that grade shall be to the flag officer of the nationality of the port.

6. When a ship of the Navy falls in at sea with a foreign warship displaying the flag of a flag officer, an exchange of salutes shall be fired; the junior saluting first. Such salutes shall be exchanged only between the senior United States ship and the senior foreign ship. Should flag officers be of the same grade and their relative rank be unknown or in doubt, they should mutually salute without delay.

7. The provisions of this article shall be subject to the provisions of article 2128.4.

2124. Notification of Gun Salute.

Whenever practicable, an official or officer to be saluted shall be notified of the salute and the time that it is to be fired.

2125. Procedure During a Gun Salute.

1. The interval between guns in salutes normally shall be five seconds.

2. During the gun salute, persons on the quarter-deck, or in the ceremonial party if ashore, shall render the hand salute; other persons on deck, or in the vicinity of the ceremonial party if ashore, shall stand at attention.

3. Officers being saluted shall render the hand salute during the firing of the gun salute.

4. The boat or vehicle in which a person being saluted is embarked shall be stopped, if practicable to do so, during the firing of the gun salute.

2126. Inability to Render or Return a Gun Salute (omitted).

2127. Returning Gun Salutes (omitted).

2128. Restrictions on Gun Salutes (omitted).

Official	Uniform	Ruffles and flourishes	Music	Guard	Remarks
President	As prescribed by senior officer present.	4	National anthem	Full	Man rail, unless otherwise directed by senior officer present.
Secretary of State when special foreign representative of the President.	do	4	do	do	Crew at quarters.
Vice President	Of the day		do	do	Do.
Secretary of Defense, Deputy Secretary of Defense, or Secretary of the Navy.	do		do	do	Do.
An assistant Secretary of Defense, Under Secretary or an Assistant Secretary of the Navy.	do		do	do	Do.

Section 5—Passing Honors

2130. "Passing Honors" and "Close Aboard" Defined.

"Passing honors" are those honors, other than gun salutes, rendered on occasions when ships or embarked officials or officers pass, or are passed, close aboard. "Close aboard" shall mean passing within six hundred yards for ships and four hundred yards for boats. These rules shall be interpreted liberally, to insure that appropriate honors are rendered.

2131. Passing Honors between Ships.

1. Passing honors, consisting of sounding "Attention" and rendering the hand salute by all persons in view on deck and not in ranks, shall be exchanged between ships of the Navy, and between ships of the Navy and the Coast Guard, passing close aboard.

2. In addition, the honors prescribed in the table on page 194 shall be rendered by a ship of the Navy passing close aboard a ship or naval station displaying the flag of the officials indicated therein; and by naval stations, insofar as practicable, when a ship displaying such flag passes close aboard. These honors shall be acknowledged by rendering the same honors in return.

2132. Passing Honors to Officials and Officers Embarked in Boats.

1. The honors prescribed in the table on page 196 shall be rendered by a ship of the Navy being passed close aboard by a boat displaying the flag or pennant of officials and officers.

2. Persons on the quarter-deck shall salute when a boat displaying a miniature of a flag or pennant passes close aboard.

2133. Passing Honors to Foreign Dignitaries and Warships.

Official	Ruffles and flourishes	Music	Guard	Remarks
President	4	National anthem	Full	"Attention" sounded, and salute by all persons in view on deck. If directed by the senior officer present, man rail.
Secretary of State when special foreign representative of President.	4	do	do	"Attention" sounded, and salute by all persons in view on deck.
Vice-President, Secretary of Defense, Deputy Secretary of Defense, Secretary of the Navy, an Assistant Secretary of Defense, Under Secretary or an Assistant Secretary of the Navy.	4	Admiral's march	do	Do.
Other civil official entitled to honors on official visit.	......	......	......	Do.
Officer of an armed service	......	......	......	Do.

1. The honors prescribed for the President of the United States shall be rendered by a ship of the Navy being passed close aboard by a ship or boat displaying the flag or standard of a foreign president, sovereign, or member of a reigning royal family, except that the foreign national anthem shall be played in lieu of the National Anthem of the United States.

2. Passing honors shall be exchanged with foreign warships passed close aboard and shall consist of parading the guard of the day, sounding "Attention," rendering the salute by all persons in view on deck, and playing the foreign national anthem.

2134. Sequence in Rendering Passing Honors.*

1. "Attention" shall be sounded by the junior when the bow of one ship passes the bow or stern of the other, or, if a senior be embarked in a boat, before the boat is abreast, or nearest to abreast, the quarter-deck.

2. The guard, if required, shall present arms, and all persons in view on deck shall salute.

3. The music, if required, shall sound off.

4. "Carry on" shall be sounded when the prescribed honors have been rendered and acknowledged.

2135. Dispensing with Passing Honors.

1. Passing honors shall not be rendered after sunset or before 0800 except when international courtesy requires.

2. Passing honors shall not be exchanged between ships of the Navy engaged in tactical evolutions outside port.

3. The senior officer present may direct that passing honors be dispensed with in whole or in part.

2136. Crew at Quarters on Entering or Leaving Port.

The crew shall normally be paraded at quarters on en-

*See Chapter 9, *Shipboard Procedures,* NWP 50, for more details.

tering or leaving port during daylight, except when undesirable to do so due to weather or other circumstances.

Section 6—Official Visits and Calls

2138. Definitions.

1. The term "official visit" shall be construed to mean a formal visit of courtesy requiring special honors and ceremonies.

2. The term "call" shall be construed to mean an informal visit of courtesy requiring no special ceremonies.

Arts. 2139, 2140, 2141—For ready reference see fold out sheet between pages 202 and 203.

2142. Table of Precedence of Diplomatic and Consular Representatives (omitted).

2143. Official Visits to the President and to Civil Officials of the Navy (omitted).

2144. Official Visits and Calls among Officers of the Naval Service.

1. An officer assuming command shall, at the first opportunity thereafter, make an official visit to the senior to whom he has reported for duty in command, and to any successor of that senior; except that for shore commands a call shall be made in lieu of such official visit.

2. Unless dispensed with by the senior, calls shall be made:

(a) By the commander of an arriving unit upon his immediate superior in the chain of command if present; and, when circumstances permit, upon the senior officer present.

(b) By an officer in command upon an immediate superior in the chain of command on the arrival of the latter.

(c) By an officer who has been the senior officer present, upon his successor.

(d) By the commander of a unit arriving at a naval

base or station upon the commander of such base or station; except that when the former is senior, the latter shall make the call.

(e) By an officer reporting for duty, upon his commanding officer.

3. When arrivals occur after 1600, or on Sunday, or on a holiday, the required calls may be postponed until the next working day.

2145. Official Visits or Calls between Officers of the Naval Service and Other Armed Services.

When in the vicinity of a command of another armed service of the United States, the senior officer present in the naval service shall arrange with the commander concerned for the exchange of official visits, or calls, as appropriate.

2146. Official Visits with United States Diplomatic and Consular Representatives (omitted).

2147. Official Visits with Governors of United States Territories and Possessions (omitted).

2148. Official Visits with Foreign Officials and Officers (omitted).

2149. Uniform for Official Visits.

Unless otherwise prescribed by the senior concerned:

1. A junior making an official visit shall wear the uniform prescribed in the tables of this chapter opposite the grade of the senior to whom the visit is made.

2. A senior returning an official visit shall wear the uniform corresponding to that which the junior has worn.

3. An officer receiving an official visit, and all participants in the reception, including the crew if paraded, shall wear the uniform prescribed in the tables of this chapter opposite the grade of the official or officer from whom the visit is received.

4. Boat crews shall wear the uniform corresponding to that worn by the senior officer embarked.

2150. Honors on Departure for, or Return from, an Official Visit.

An officer leaving or returning to his flagship or command upon the occasion of an official visit shall be rendered the honors prescribed for an official visit except that, aboard his flagship, the uniform of the day normally shall be worn and gun salutes shall not be fired.

2151. Procedure for Official Visits.

1. The honors prescribed for an official visit shall be rendered on arrival as follows:

(a) When the rail is manned, men shall be uniformly spaced at the rail on each weather deck, facing outboard.

(b) "Attention" shall be sounded as the visitor's boat or vehicle approaches the ship.

(c) If a gun salute is prescribed on arrival, it shall be fired as the visitor approaches and is still clear of the side. The prescribed flag or pennant shall be broken on the first gun and shall continue to fly on the visited ship until the departure of the visitor. Other ships firing a concurrent salute shall on the last gun haul down the flag or pennant displayed in honor of the visitor. If the ship being visited is moored to a pier in such a position that it is not practicable to render the gun salute prior to the arrival on board, the salute shall be rendered, provided local regulations do not forbid gun salutes, after the official has arrived on board and the commanding officer has assured himself that the official and his party are moved to a position in the ship that is well clear of the saluting battery.

(d) The boat or vehicle shall be piped as it comes alongside.

(e) The visitor shall be piped over the side, and all persons on the quarter-deck shall salute and the guard shall present arms until the termination of the pipe

flourishes, music, or gun salute, whichever shall be the last rendered.

(f) The piping of the side, the ruffles and flourishes, and the music shall be rendered in the order named. In the absence of a band, "To the Colors" shall be sounded by a bugle in lieu of the national anthem, when required.

(g) The visitor, if entitled to 11 guns or more, shall be invited to inspect the guard upon completion of such honors as may be rendered. If the guard consists of the United States Marines, the band shall, during this inspection of the Marine Guard, play "The Marines' Hymn."

2. The honors prescribed for an official visit shall be rendered on departure as follows:

(a) The rail shall be manned, if required.

(b) "Attention" shall be sounded as the visitor arrives on the quarter-deck.

(c) At the end of leave taking, the guard shall present arms, all persons on the quarter-deck shall salute, and the ruffles and flourishes, followed by the music, shall be rendered. As the visitor enters the line of side boys, he shall be piped over the side. The salute and present arms shall terminate with the pipe; and, unless a gun salute is to be fired, a flag or pennant displayed in honor of the visitor shall be hauled down.

(d) The boat or vehicle shall be piped away from the side.

(e) If a gun salute is prescribed on departure, it shall be fired when the visitor is clear of the side and the flag or pennant displayed in honor of the visitor shall be hauled down with the last gun of the salute.

3. The same honors and ceremonies as for an official visit to a ship of the Navy shall be rendered, insofar as practicable and appropriate, on the occasion of an official visit to a naval station.

2152. Returning Official Visits and Calls.

1. An official visit shall be returned within twenty-four

hours, when practicable.

2. A flag or general officer shall, circumstances permitting, return the official visits of officers of the grade of captain in the Navy or senior thereto, and to officials of corresponding grade. He may send his chief of staff to return other official visits.

3. Officers other than flag or general officers shall personally return all official visits.

4. Flag and general officers may expect official visits to be returned in person by foreign governors, officers, and other high officials except chiefs of state. Other officers may expect such visits to be returned by suitable representatives.

5. Calls made by juniors upon seniors in the naval service shall be returned as courtesy requires and circumstances permit; calls made by persons not in the naval service shall be returned.

2153. Side Honors.

1. On the arrival and departure of civil officials and foreign officers, and of United States officers when so directed by the senior officer present, the side shall be piped and the appropriate number of side boys paraded.

2. Officers appropriate to the occasion shall attend the side on the arrival and departure of officials and officers.

2154. Dispensing with Side Boys and Guard and Band.

1. Side boys shall not be paraded on Sunday, or on other days between sunset and 0800, or during meal hours of the crew, general drills and evolutions, and periods of regular overhaul; except in honor of civil officials or foreign officers, when they may be paraded at any time during daylight.

2. Except for official visits and other formal occasions, side boys shall not be paraded in honor of officers of the armed services of the United States, unless otherwise directed by the senior officer present.

2140. Table of Honors for Official Visits of United States Civil (
Except as modified or dispensed with by these regulation[s]
station on the occasion of the official visit of the following Un[ited]
below, shall be fired on arrival instead of on departure):

Official	Uniform	Gun salute Arrival	Gun salute Departure	Ruffles and flourishes	Music	G
President	Full dress	21	21	4	National anthem.	F
Ex-President or President-elect	do	21	21	4	Admiral's march.	..
Secretary of State when acting as special foreign representative of the President.	do	19	19	4	National anthem.	..
Vice President	do		19	4	Admiral's march.	..
Speaker of the House of Representatives.	do		19	4	do	..
Governor of a State of the United States.	do		19	4	do	..
Chief Justice of the United States.	do		19	4	do	..
Ambassador, High Commissioner, or special diplomatic representative whose credentials give him authority equal to or greater than that of an Ambassador.	do		19	4	National anthem.	..
Secretary of Defense	do	19	19	4	Admiral's march.	..
Deputy Secretary of Defense	do	19	19	4	do	..
Cabinet officer (other than Secretary of Defense)	Dress		19	4	do	..
Secretary of the Navy	Full dress	19	19	4	do	..
Secretary of the Army, Secretary of the Air Force	Dress		19	4	do	..
President pro tempore of the Senate.	do		19	4	do	..
Assistant Secretaries of Defense	do	17	17	4	do	..
Under Secretary and Assistant Secretaries of the Navy.	do	17	17	4	do	..
Under Secretary or Assistant Secretary of the Army or the Air Force.	do		17	4	do	..
Governor General or Governor of a Territory or possession of the United States, or area un-	do		17	4	do	..

fficials.

the honors prescribed in this table shall be rendered by a ship or ted States civil officials (ashore, the single gun salute, when prescribed

uard	Side boys	Crew	Within what limits	Flag		
				What	Where	During
ll...	8	Man rail		President's	Main truck.	Visit.
do...	8	Quarters		National	do	Salute.
do...	8	do		Secretary's	do	Visit.
do...	8	do		Vice President's.	do	Do.
do...	8			National	Fore truck.	Salute.
do...	8		Area under his jurisdiction.	do	do	Do.
do...	8			do	do	Do.
do...	8		Nation or nations to which accredited.	do	do	Do.
do...	8	Quarters		Secretary's	Main truck.	Visit.
do...	8	do		Deputy Secretary's	do	Do.
do...	8			National	Fore truck.	Salute.
do...	8	Quarters		Secretary's	Main truck.	Visit.
do...	8			National	Fore truck.	Salute.
do...	8			do	do	Do.
do...	8	Quarters		Assistant Secretary's.	Main truck.	Visit.
do...	8	do		Under Secretary's or Assistant Secretary's.	do	Do.
do...	8			National	Fore truck.	Salute.
do...	8		Area under his jurisdiction.	do	do	Do.

3. Side boys shall not be paraded in honor of an officer of the armed services in civilian clothes, unless such officer is at the time acting in an official civil capacity.

4. The side shall be piped when side boys are paraded, but not at other times.

5. The guard and band shall not be paraded in honor of the arrival or departure of an individual at times when side boys in his honor are dispensed with.

Section 7—Formal Occasions Other Than Official Visits

2156. Honors to an Official Entitled to 19 or More Guns (omitted).

2157. Honors for a Flag or General Officer, or Unit Commander, Assuming or Relieving Command (omitted).

2158. Honors at Official Inspection.

1. When a flag officer or unit commander boards a ship of the Navy to make an official inspection, honors shall be rendered as for an official visit, except that the uniform shall be as prescribed by the inspecting officer. His flag or command pennant shall be broken upon his arrival, unless otherwise prescribed in these regulations, and shall be hauled down on his departure.

2. The provisions of this article shall apply, insofar as practicable and appropriate, when a flag or general officer, in command ashore, makes an official inspection of a unit of his command.

2159. Honors for a Civil Official Taking Passage (omitted).

Section 8—Display of Flags and Pennants (omitted—covered in Chapter on Flags and Pennants)

Section 9—Special Ceremonies, Anniversaries, and Solemnities (omitted)

Section 10—Deaths and Funerals (omitted)

Chapter XV

FLAGS, PENNANTS AND BOAT HAILS

"Each person in the naval service, upon coming on board a ship of the Navy, shall salute the national ensign if it is flying. He shall stop on reaching the upper platform of the accommodation ladder, or the shipboard end of the brow, face the national ensign, and render the salute, after which he shall salute the officer of the deck. On leaving the ship, he shall render the salutes in inverse order. The officer of the deck shall return both salutes in each case.

"The salutes prescribed in this article shall also be rendered to foreign national ensigns and aboard foreign men-of-war."—*U.S. Navy Regulations, 1948* (Art. 21-08).

Closely related to and, in fact, overlapping the subject of honors and ceremonies is the subject of flags and pennants. This chapter will serve as a guide to the Officer of the Deck on the usage and customs related thereto. The material is largely based on *U.S. Naval Flags and Pennants* (DNC 27), and *U.S. Navy Regulations, 1948*. The former publication is not as well known as it might be; it should be studied by every officer aboard ship who stands deck watches. Only the most basic and commonly used information will be presented here as a ready reference.

Many countries have variations to their national flag that are authorized for specific uses. The national flag used by men-of-war only is the *ensign;* that used by merchant ships is the *merchant flag*. The United States of America has only one flag, the *national colors,* which is used for all purposes. It may properly be called the *ensign* when used in the Navy.

Each landing party battalion that may be sent ashore from a ship has the national colors and an organization color, the U.S. Navy infantry battalion flag. Each company, when parading ashore and at other ceremonies, may display a *guidon.*

GENERAL RULES FOR DISPLAY

The distinctive mark of a ship or craft of the Navy in commission is a personal flag or command pennant of an officer of the Navy, or a commission pennant. The distinctive mark of a hospital ship of the Navy, in commission in time of war, is the Red Cross flag. Not more than one distinctive mark is displayed by a ship or craft at the same time, nor are the commission pennant and the personal flag of a civil official displayed simultaneously.

(a) Except as prescribed in Navy Regulations for certain occasions of ceremony and when civil officials are embarked, the distinctive mark mentioned above is displayed day and night at the after masthead or, in a mastless ship, from the loftiest and most conspicuous hoist.

When the ship is not underway, the national ensign and the union jack are displayed from 0800 until sunset from the flagstaff and the jackstaff, respectively. A ship which enters port at night displays, when appropriate, the national ensign from the gaff at daylight for a time sufficient to establish her nationality; it is customary for other ships of war to display their national ensigns in return.

The national ensign is displayed during daylight from the gaff of a ship underway under the following circumstances, unless or as otherwise directed by the senior officer present:

(a) Getting underway and coming to anchor
(b) Falling in with other ships
(c) Cruising near land
(d) During battle.

The union jack displayed from the jackstaff is the size of the union of the national ensign displayed from the flagstaff.

SPECIAL RULES FOR U. S. ENSIGN

During Gun Salutes

A ship of the U.S. Navy displays the national ensign at a masthead while firing a salute in honor of a United States national anniversary or official, as follows:

(a) At the main during the national salute prescribed for the 22nd of February and the 4th of July
(b) At the main during a 21-gun salute to a United States civil official, except by a ship displaying the personal flag of the official being saluted
(c) At the fore during a salute to any other United States civil official, except by a ship which is displaying the personal flag of the official being saluted.

During a gun salute, the national ensign shall remain displayed from the gaff or the flagstaff, in addition to its display as prescribed above.

In Boats

The national ensign is displayed from waterborne boats of the Navy:

(a) When underway during daylight in a foreign port
(b) When ships are required to be dressed or full-dressed
(c) When going alongside a foreign vessel
(d) When an officer or official is embarked on an official occasion

(e) When a flag or general officer, a unit commander, a commanding officer, or a chief of staff, in uniform, is embarked in a boat of his command or in one assigned to his personal use

(f) At such other times as may be prescribed by the senior officer present.

Since small boats are a part of a vessel, they follow the motions of the parent vessel as regards the half-masting of colors.

Dipping

When any vessel, under United States registry, or under the registry of a nation formally recognized by the government of the United States, salutes a ship of the U.S. Navy by dipping her ensign, it is answered dip for dip. If the national ensign is not already being displayed, it is hoisted especially for the purpose of answering the dip; the dip is returned, and, after a suitable interval, the ensign is hauled down. An ensign being displayed at half-mast is hoisted to the truck or peak before a dip is answered.

No ship of the Navy dips the national ensign unless in return for such compliment.

Of the colors carried by a naval force on shore, only the battalion or regimental colors are dipped in rendering or acknowledging a salute.

Half-Masting

In half-masting the national ensign it is, if not previously hoisted, first hoisted to the truck or peak and then lowered to half-mast. Before lowering from half-mast, the ensign is hoisted to the truck or peak and then lowered.

When the national ensign is half-masted, the union jack, if displayed from the jackstaff, is likewise half-masted.

At noon on Memorial Day, May 30, each saluting ship, fires a salute of 21 minute-guns. All ships display the national ensign at half-mast from 0800 until the completion of the salute, or until 1220 if no salute is fired.

Following Motions of Senior Officer Present

On board ship upon all occasions of hoisting, lowering, or half-masting the national ensign, the motions of the senior officer present are followed, except as prescribed for answering a dip or firing a gun salute.

A ship displaying the flag of the President, Secretary of Defense, Deputy Secretary of Defense, Secretary of the Navy, an Assistant Secretary of Defense, Under Secretary of the Navy, or an Assistant Secretary of the Navy is regarded as the ship of the senior officer present.

Size of Colors to Be Prescribed

When two or more vessels are in company in port, the senior officer present makes a preparatory signal at 0745, giving the size of colors to be hoisted at 0800. If such a signal indicating size of colors is made at any other time during the day, colors shall be shifted when the signal is hauled down.

Display of Colors During Gun Salutes

While firing a salute to a foreign nation in one of its ports, while returning such a salute fired by a foreign warship, or while firing a salute on the occasion of a foreign national anniversary, celebration, or solemnity, a ship displays the ensign of the foreign nation at the main truck.

While firing a salute to a foreign dignitary or official entitled to 21 guns, a ship displays the national ensign of such dignitary or official at the main truck. While firing a salute to a foreign official entitled to less than 21 guns, or to a foreign officer, or when returning a salute fired by a foreign officer, the national ensign of the foreign official or officer is displayed at the foretruck.

DISPLAY OF UNITED NATIONS FLAG

The following policy concerning the display of the United Nations flag is quoted from a Department of Defense directive:

"1. The United Nations flag will be displayed at installations of the armed forces of the United States only upon occasion of visits of high dignitaries of the United Nations while in performance of their official duties with the United Nations, or on other special occasions in honor of the United Nations. When so displayed it will be displayed with the United States flag, both flags will be of the same approximate size and on the same level, the flag of the United States in the position of honor on the right (observer's left).

"2. The United Nations flag will be carried by troops on occasions when the United Nations or high dignitaries thereof are to be honored. When so carried, the United Nations flag will be carried on the marching left of the United States flag and other United States colors or standards normally carried by such troops.

"3. On occasions similar to those referred to in paragraph 2, above, U.S. Naval vessels will display the United Nations flag in the same manner as is prescribed for a foreign ensign during visits of a foreign President or Sovereign.

"4. Except as indicated in paragraphs 1, 2, and 3, above, the United Nations flag will be displayed by United States Armed Forces only when so authorized by the President of the United States."

U.S. Naval vessels authorized to display the United Nations flag display it in the same manner as is prescribed for a foreign ensign during visits of a foreign president or sovereign.

PERSONAL FLAGS AND PENNANTS

Afloat

Except as otherwise prescribed in *Navy Regulations,* a flag officer or a unit commander afloat displays his personal flag or command pennant from his flagship. At no time does he display it from more than one ship.

When a flag officer eligible for command at sea is embarked for passage in a ship of the Navy, his personal flag is displayed from such ship, unless there is already displayed from such ship the flag of an officer his senior.

Flags or pennants of officers not eligible for command at sea are not displayed from ships of the United States Navy.

Broad and Burgee Command Pennants

The broad or burgee command pennant is the personal command pennant of an officer of the Navy, not a flag officer, commanding a unit of ships or aircraft.

The broad command pennant indicates command of:

(a) A division of battleships, aircraft carriers, or cruisers
(b) A force, flotilla, or squadron of ships or craft of any type
(c) An aircraft wing.

The burgee command pennant indicates command of:

(a) A division of ships or craft other than battleships, aircraft carriers, or cruisers
(b) A major subdivision of an aircraft wing.

The broad and burgee command pennants are surcharged with numerals to indicate the organizational number within a type. Where two commanders within a type are entitled to display the same command pennant and when they have the same organizational number in different echelons of command, the commander in the higher echelon uses Roman numerals in the surcharge. In all other cases, Arabic numerals are used. Blue numerals are used on broad command pennants, and red numerals on burgee command pennants.

When the National Ensign Is at Masthead

The President's flag, if displayed at a masthead where a national ensign is required to be displayed during an official visit or during periods of dressing or full-dressing ship, shall remain at that masthead to port of the United States national ensign and to starboard of a foreign national ensign.

Except as provided above, a personal flag or command pennant is not displayed at the same masthead with a national ensign, but:

(a) During a gun salute, it should be lowered clear of the ensign
(b) During an official visit, it should be shifted to the starboard yardarm in a single-masted ship and to the foretruck in a two-masted ship
(c) During periods of dressing or full-dressing ship:
  (1) If displayed from the foretruck or from the masthead of a single-masted ship, it should be shifted to the starboard yardarm
  (2) If displayed from the maintruck, it should be shifted to the foretruck in lieu of the national ensign at that mast
  (3) If displayed from the after truck of a ship with more than two masts, it should remain at the after truck in lieu of the national ensign at that mast.

Flags or Pennants in Boats, Automobiles, and Aircraft

When embarked in a boat of the Naval Service on official occasions, an officer in command, or a chief of staff when acting for him, displays from the bow his personal flag or command pennant, or if not entitled to either, a commission pennant.

An officer entitled to the display of a personal flag or command pennant may display a miniature of such flag or pennant in the vicinity of the coxswain's station when embarked on other than official occasions in a boat of the Naval Service.

An officer entitled to the display of a personal flag or command pennant may, when riding in an automobile on an official occasion, display such flag or pennant forward on such vehicle.

All flag officers are authorized to show stars of their rank on their assigned automobiles. The method of showing such stars is confined to 6″ x 9″ plates to be attached to license plates or located in the general vicinity of the license plates. Stars or replicas of personal flags are not painted on automobiles.

Personal flags or pennants may be painted on aircraft assigned to flag officers or to officers acting in flag billets. Sheet metal replicas inserted in metal slots are also authorized. The flags or pennants should be located on each side of the forward fuselage and should be 11 by 14 inches.

Half-Masting

Personal flags, command pennants, and commission pennants should not be displayed at half-mast for a deceased official or officer except as prescribed in *Navy Regulations*.

For United Nations or North Atlantic Treaty Organization Officials

Personal flags of United Nations or North Atlantic Treaty Organization officials are not displayed when these officers are embarked in U.S. Naval vessels unless the officer holding such office qualifies for displaying his personal flag by being a U.S. Navy flag officer eligible for command at sea.

MISCELLANEOUS FLAGS AND PENNANTS

Absence Indicators

In ships, the absence of a chief of staff or a commanding officer is indicated from sunrise to sunset by the display of an absence indicator as prescribed in the table shown on the next page. Substitute pennants as shown in the signal book are used.

In the case of the absence of a commanding officer who is acting as a temporary unit commander, both absentee pennants should be displayed.

Intention to Depart Officially

In port the display of the speed pennant (where best seen) indicates that the official or officer whose personal flag or command pennant is displayed will leave the ship officially in about five minutes. When hauled down it means the official or officer is departing.

Church Pennant

Public Law 829 authorizes the use of the church pennant above the ensign "during church services conducted by naval chaplains at sea." The words "at sea" are interpreted for U.S. Navy purposes as meaning "on board a naval vessel." Shore stations, while not authorized to display the church pennant above the ensign, may display it separately if desired.

Ships are fitted with two halyards to the same point of hoist at the staff and gaff; this permits the display of the church pennant and the ensign simultaneously.

If divine services are being conducted at the time of morning colors, or if they begin at that time, the ensign is hoisted to the peak at the prescribed time. The church pennant is then hoisted and the ensign dipped just clear of the church pennant.

Should the ensign be displayed at half-mast, the church pennant should be hoisted just above the ensign.

Sub.	Indication	Where normally displayed	Absentee
1st	Absence of an official from his ship for a period of 72 hours or less	Starboard main yardarm (outboard)	Absence of a flag officer or unit commander whose personal flag or command pennant is flying in this ship.
2nd	Same as 1st substitute	Port main yardarm (inboard)	Absence of chief of staff
3rd	Same as 1st substitute	Port main yardarm (outboard)	Absence of Captain (executive officer if Captain is absent for a period exceeding 72 hours)
4th	Same as 1st substitute	Starboard main yardarm (inboard)	Absence of civil or military official whose flag is flying in this ship

Should divine services be conducted during time of evening colors, the church pennant is hauled down and the ensign hoisted to the peak just prior to the time for colors: the ensign is then hauled down at the prescribed time.

Union Jack for General Court-Martial

The union jack is displayed at a yardarm to denote that a general court-martial or court of inquiry is in session. It is hoisted when the court meets and hauled down when the court adjourns.

Meal Break

When the ship is at anchor, the meal break (crew's meal indicator) is displayed between sunrise and sunset on either yardarm during the crew's meal period. The meal break is the E flag.

Battle Efficiency Pennant (Meat Ball)

The battle efficiency pennant is flown at the foretruck from sunrise to sunset, while at anchor, during the period provided in *Awards for Intra-Type Competition.*

When a guard flag, ready-duty flag, or Presidential Unit Citation pennant is displayed at the foretruck with the battle efficiency pennant, the latter should be flown below such other flag. The battle efficiency pennant is hauled down while Baker is being displayed at the foretruck.

Homeward Bound Pennant

The use of the "homeward bound" pennant is traditional. The specifications of the design and rules for display apparently have never been adequately set forth; however, the usage set forth in DNC 27 is believed to conform with tradition.

Presidential Unit Citation (PUC) Pennant

At anchor, ships awarded the Presidential Unit Citation

should fly the pennant, described in DNC 27, at the foretruck from sunrise to sunset.

Convoy Commodore Flag

The Convoy Commodore's flag is to be flown by the commodore's ship while the convoy is forming up or reforming or whenever the commodore wishes to make his ship readily identifiable.

It is flown on similar occasions by the vice or rear commodore's ship when such officer has assumed command of the convoy or is acting independently of the commodore when in charge of some portion of the convoy.

DRESSING AND FULL-DRESSING SHIP

Ships not underway are dressed or full-dressed from 0800 until sunset when prescribed or when directed. Ships underway are not dressed or full-dressed.

When full-dressing is prescribed, the senior officer present may direct that dressing be substituted if, in his opinion, the state of the weather makes such action advisable. He may also, under such circumstances, direct that the ensigns be hauled down from the mastheads after being hoisted.

(See DNC 27 for details of dressing and full-dressing, including the specified sequence of signal flags and pennants to be hoisted.)

BOAT HAILS

All boats approaching a ship at night should be hailed as soon as they are within hearing distance. The watch aboard ship will call out "Boat ahoy!" The coxswain will reply as shown in table on the next page to indicate the rank of the senior officer or official in the boat.

Officer or Official	Coxswain's reply
The President or Vice President of the U.S.	"UNITED STATES"
Secretary of Defense, Deputy or Assistant Secretary of Defense	"DEFENSE"
The Secretary, Under Secretary, or Assistant Secretary of the Navy	"NAVY"
Chief of Naval Operations, Vice Chief of Naval Operations	"NAVAL OPERATIONS"
Fleet or Force Commander	"FLEET" OR ABBREVIATION OF ADMINISTRATIVE TITLE
A General Officer	"GENERAL OFFICER"
A Chief of Staff	"STAFF"
A Flotilla Commander	*"_____ FLOT _____" (Type) (number)
A Squadron Commander	*"_____ RON _____" (Type) (number)
A Division Commander	*"_____ DIV _____" (Type) (number)
A Marine Officer Commanding a Brigade	"BRIGADE COMMANDER"
A Commanding Officer of a Ship	"_____" (NAME OF SHIP)
A Marine Officer Commanding a Regiment	"REGIMENTAL COMMANDER"
Any other Commissioned Officer	"AYE, AYE"
Other Officers (not commissioned)	"NO, NO"
Enlisted men	"HELLO"
A boat not intending to go alongside, regardless of rank of passenger	"PASSING"

* The type abbreviation is used; i.e., DesFlot-2, DesRon-6, DesDiv-22.

During hours when honors are rendered, the Officer of the Deck should challenge an approaching boat as soon as possible by raising his arm with closed fist in the direction of the boat and should train a long glass or binoculars on the coxswain. The coxswain should reply by holding up the number of fingers corresponding to the number, if any, of side boys which should be standing by to honor the senior officer in his boat. A wave-off from the coxswain would indicate no side boys are required.

BOAT GONGS

For the benefit of officers on board who need to know, the Officer of the Deck should indicate the arrival and departure of Commanders, Chiefs of Staff, and Commanding Officers as follows:

Over the loudspeaker system, sound the boat gong, special gong, or chemical alarm (as specified locally) in groups of two, corresponding to the number of side boys to which the officer announced is entitled, followed by the announcement of the officer's organization as taken from the coxswain's reply above.

Chapter XVI

RULES OF THE NAUTICAL ROAD

"He (the officer of the deck) shall thoroughly familiarize himself with the laws to prevent collision and shall strictly comply with them."—*U.S. Navy Regulations, 1948* (Art. 1010).

This chapter is a guide and ready reference for the Officer of the Deck as to the rules to prevent collisions—rules which are required to be followed while navigating or piloting upon the high seas and the adjacent inland waters of the United States. It will be noted that vessels and seaplanes navigating the high seas are required to follow the International Rules, while vessels navigating inshore of the boundary lines dividing the high seas from inland waters are required to follow the Inland Rules and the Pilot Rules established pursuant thereto. These statutory and regulatory Rules are to be found in CG-169, entitled *Rules to Prevent Collisions of Vessels and Pilot Rules for Certain Inland Waters of the Atlantic and Pacific Coasts and of the Gulf of Mexico,* and Farwell-Prunski's *Rules of the Nautical Road.* The latter publication is of special value to the Officer of the Deck in that it contains a thorough, up-to-date treatment of the practical and legal aspects of the subject, as well as the material published by the Commandant, U.S. Coast Guard, in CG-169.

The material presented here incorporates the latest changes in the International and Inland Rules, including the revised International Rules effective January 1, 1954. A number of important definitions are listed first. These are then followed by a brief summation of the most important aspects of the Rules of the Road, as well as some useful axioms. Commonly observed light displays, daymarks, and sound signals are presented next. The last item in the chapter is a summation of the changes in the International Rules brought about by the 1948 International Conference, which should be of benefit to the Officer of the Deck familiar with the International Rules in effect prior to January 1, 1954.

DEFINITIONS

VESSEL	This term includes every description of watercraft, other than a seaplane on the water, used or capable of being used as a means of transportation on water.
SEAPLANE	An aircraft designed to maneuver on the water.
POWER-DRIVEN VESSEL	Defined in the International Rules as any vessel propelled by machinery—including one partially propelled by sail.
STEAM VESSEL	Defined in the Inland Rules as any vessel propelled by machinery, including one partially propelled by sail; i.e., a power-driven vessel as defined by the International Rules.
PRIVILEGED VESSEL	A vessel which is required to *hold course and speed.*
BURDENED VESSEL	A vessel which is required to *keep clear* of a privileged vessel.
UNDER WAY	Said of a vessel or seaplane on the water which is not at anchor, made fast to the shore, or aground.
CROSS SIGNALS	An illegal response of one blast on the whistle or siren to a signal of

two blasts, or vice versa, by a steam vessel in inland waters.

MODERATE SPEED Ordinarily, bare steerageway or such speed as will enable a vessel proceeding in fog or other similarly restricted visibility to stop in one half the distance of visibility; in extremely close visibility, the requirement to moor, come to anchor, or not to get under way.

IN EXTREMIS A crossing, meeting, or overtaking situation which has developed to such a dangerous degree that both vessels must take prompt and effective steps to avoid collision.

IMPORTANT ASPECTS OF THE RULES

BOUNDARY LINES Specific boundary lines of inland waters have been established in most of the areas subject to the Inland Rules. These may be obtained by reference to CG-169 or Farwell-Prunski's *Rules of the Nautical Road.* In areas where no specific boundary lines have been established, boundary lines of inland waters are determined by:

(1) The shore line;

(2) At buoyed entrances, a line approximately parallel with the general trend of the shore, drawn through the outermost buoy or other aid to navigation.

As Officer of the Deck, it is important that you know where the boundary lines dividing the high seas from inland waters are. The Inland Rules and the Pilot Rules for Inland Waters apply *inshore* of these lines. On the other hand, the International Rules apply *outside* these lines. If you do not know where they are, the actions, lights, and sound signals of vessels approaching your vessel from the other side of a boundary line may mislead you.

PASSING SIGNALS

There is a fundamental difference in the meaning and the method of prescribing the conventional one-and-two-short-blast passing signals under International and Inland Rules. Under the International Rules, the signals are purely rudder signals, to be given when, and only when, a change in course is intended. Accordingly, a general rule is stated in these Rules which provides for a signal in every situation when the course is changed. Under the Inland and Pilot Rules, on the other hand, the one-and-two-short-blast signals are not for the purpose of announcing a change in course, but to indicate the side on which an approaching vessel will pass. In these Rules, it is, therefore, necessary to specify the use of a signal in a particular situation. The appropriate signal is not covered by a general rule, but is prescribed in the rule referring to a specific situation, and is required to be given and answered, when possible, before the vessels approach within one-half mile of each other, whether a change of course is involved or not.

LIGHTS

(Two recent opinions concerning lights expressed by the Admiralty Division of the Judge Advocate General will be of interest to all Officers of the Deck.

(1) Anchor lights are not required to be shown by a vessel in drydock unless the vessel is in an open-end dock with part of the vessel projecting out over the sill.

(2) A vessel dragging an anchor on the ground at short stay to assist in shiphandling should continue to display underway lights, not anchor lights.)

The importance of proper running and riding lights can hardly be over-emphasized. It is the function of these lights to give a vessel such timely and effective notice of the proximity of another that all doubt as to her character and intentions will be settled before there is any serious risk of collision. More than half the Rules relate to them, and, in collision cases, the courts construe strongly against vessels which disregard their requirements. You should make a special study of the differences in lights required under the International Rules, the Inland Rules, and the Pilot Rules for Inland Waters. Whether at sea or in the inland waters of the United States, the Rules concerning lights in that area must be obeyed literally in all weathers from sunset to sunrise (*not from darkness to daylight*). Moreover, during such times no other lights which may be mistaken for the prescribed lights or which impair their visibility or distinctive character, or interfere with the keeping of a proper lookout, may be exhibited. It is true that Naval and Coast Guard vessels of *special construction* are allowed to vary the number, position, range, or arc of visibility of the lights required by the Rules, *provided they maintain the closest possible compliance with the pertinent Rules,* but this is not a matter within the discretion of the Officer of the Deck or other shipboard officers. In this respect, your responsibility is limited to knowing which vessels have been found to be of special construction by the proper authorities, and what lights are carried by them.

SPEED The Rules require every vessel *in* or *near* fog, mist, falling snow, heavy rainstorms, or any other condition similarly restricting visibility to:

(1) *Go at a moderate speed,* having careful regard to the existing circumstances and conditions;

(2) *Stop her engines,* and *then navigate with caution* until danger of collision is over, upon hearing, apparently forward of her beam, the fog signal of a vessel the position of which is not ascertained.

Both these requirements are strictly enforced by the courts, and departure from them is permitted only to avoid immediate danger. Therefore, you must always proceed at moderate speed in fog; stop the engines upon hearing a fog signal forward or apparently forward of the beam; and from then on maintain bare steerageway as long as danger of collision exists. There is no general rule in either the International or Inland Rules which limits the speed of vessels in good visibility. However, every vessel is liable for damage caused by her swells, whether that damage is to property along the shore or to passing vessels and their tows. Consequently, there will be times when speed will have to be reduced in good visibility, as well as in fog.

RADAR

Court decisions have held vessels equipped with radar at fault in collisions in reduced visibility, not only for failure to use radar, but also for failure to employ it intelligently. The possession of radar does not give any vessel the right to use greater than moderate speed in restricted visibility *or* excuse her failure to have adequate and proper lookouts, to stop her engines when a fog signal is heard apparently forward of the beam, or to take all the precaution required by the practice of good seamanship. In its proper prospectus, radar is merely an additional and useful aid to navigation.

MEETING, CROSSING, AND OVERTAKING

Under International and Inland Rules alike, approaching power-driven (i.e., steam) vessels are classified as meeting, crossing, and overtaking vessels, and are required to pass each other in accordance with their respective conditions of privilege and burden. Seaplanes on the water are, in turn, required to conform to the Rules governing the actions of power-driven vessels in these three situations, while sailing vessels are given the right of way over power-driven vessels, except when overtaking them. It is, therefore, necessary that you have a clear mental picture of the meeting, crossing, and overtaking situations, and understand the conditions of privilege and burden in each, in order to be a competent Officer of the Deck.

Study Figure 1, noting that:

(1) Two power-driven vessels are held to be meeting if their courses are substantially opposite or within a point or two of being opposite, or if, as in the case of a winding river, they will become opposite at the point where they meet, even though they may first sight each other at right angles. In open water, this will be when you can see the masts of the vessel ahead in a line, or nearly in a line, with the masts on your vessel by day, and both sidelights of the vessel ahead by night. Neither vessel is privileged in this situation. On the contrary, the two

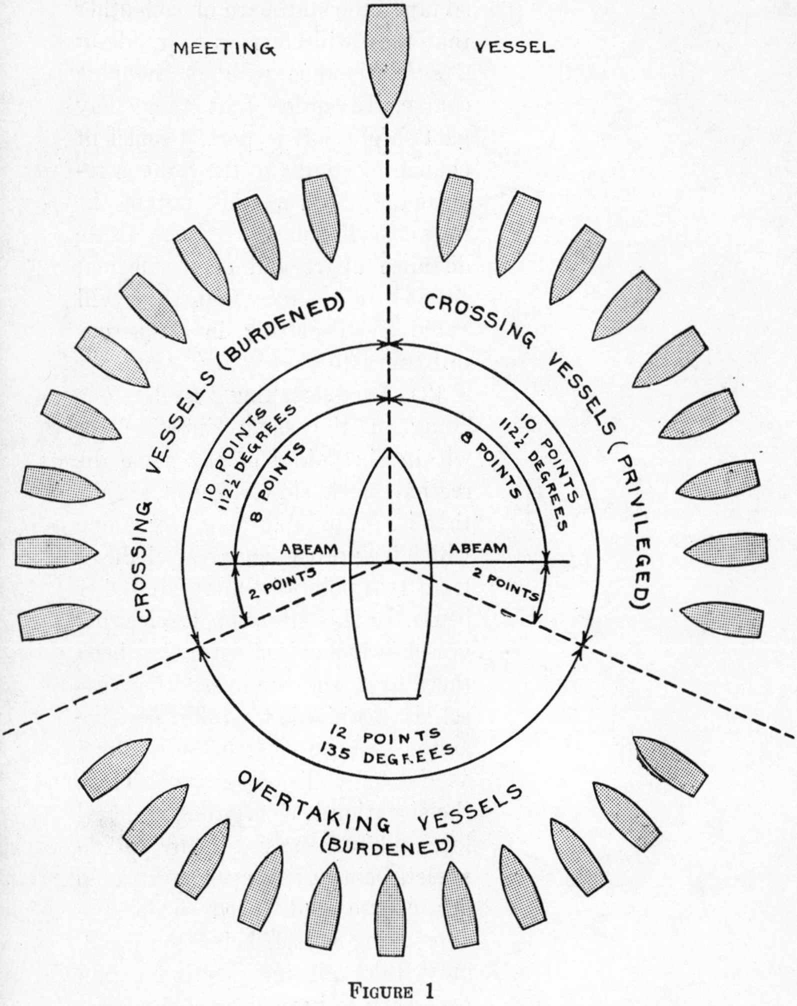
MEETING
VESSEL
CROSSING VESSELS (BURDENED)
CROSSING VESSELS (PRIVILEGED)
10 POINTS
112½ DEGREES
8 POINTS
10 POINTS
112½ DEGREES
8 POINTS
ABEAM
ABEAM
2 POINTS
2 POINTS
12 POINTS
135 DEGREES
OVERTAKING VESSELS
(BURDENED)

FIGURE 1

meeting vessels are required to pass port to port, unless they are already so far to the starboard of each other that they will clear on that side at a safe distance without changing course. In order that they may pass safely port to port, a sufficient change of course to the right is required of both vessels, not in the jaws of collision, but at such a safe distance apart and of a sufficient number of degrees that they will avoid even getting in dangerous proximity to each other.

(2) An overtaking vessel is one going in the same direction, or within six points of the same direction, as a slower vessel ahead; that is, an overtaking vessel is one which is approaching a vessel ahead from two points or more abaft her beam. In this situation the leading vessel is recognized as having been there first, and the overtaking vessel is required to take positive action to keep clear of her as long as risk of collision remains. Thus, the situation is clearly one of privilege and burden; and the overtaken vessel, being privileged, must keep her course and speed, while the overtaking vessel, being burdened, must take all the positive action necessary to keep clear of the overtaken vessel.

(3) Two power-driven vessels are

held to be crossing when one approaches the other on either side in the arc between meeting and overtaking; that is, from a point or two on the bow to two points abaft the beam. Here, too, the situation is one of privilege and burden. The privileged crossing vessel—that is, the one having the other on her port hand—is required to keep course and speed, until definite remedial action becomes necessary; while the burdened vessel is required to keep clear, to avoid crossing ahead, and if necessary, to slacken speed, stop, or reverse. It is only when the two crossing vessels have arrived in dangerous proximity that the privileged vessel in the crossing situation is allowed to take positive action to avert collision—and then, she *must* do so.

Thereupon, remember that you should always take bearings of vessels approaching or appearing to approach your vessel on either side in the arc from right ahead to two points abaft the beam. If the bearing draws forward appreciably, the other vessel will pass ahead. If it draws aft appreciably, the other vessel will pass astern. On the other hand, if the bearing remains the same, or nearly so, or changes very slowly, there is a definite risk of collision, and proper and effective action to prevent collision should be taken at once. The taking of prompt and effective action will normally avoid situations where your vessel is privileged and therefore bound to hold course and speed, while you have to "sweat out" the possibility of the burdened vessel taking action to keep clear at the last minute. This is especially true in instances where merchant vessels attempt to seize the right of way or maneuver to gain the right of way. In such instances their failure to observe the Rules does not relieve them of the responsibility they otherwise would have; but you, on the other hand, cannot maintain your course and speed into collision, either. In cases of doubt, as well as when routine meeting, crossing, and overtaking situations develop, the Commanding Officer should be notified as to what the situation is and what action has been or is being taken.

SPECIAL CIRCUMSTANCES

The International and Inland Rules both recognize that situations may arise where specific Rules will not work. And where departure from these Rules is necessary to avoid immediate danger, such action is accordingly authorized by the so-called Rule of Special Circumstances. Such departure, however, is authorized *for this purpose only*

—and then only to the extent necessary.

DANGER SIGNALS

Under the Inland Rules, the danger signal is a mandatory, all-purpose, all-weather, alarm signal of four or more short and rapid blasts, which is required to be given by every steam (i.e., power-driven) vessel in doubt as to an approaching vessel's course or intention. Under the International Rules, on the other hand, the danger signal is an optional signal of five or more short and rapid blasts, which may be given only by the privileged vessel in the overtaking and crossing situations at sea, and then only when she is in sight of another vessel and in doubt that the other vessel is taking sufficient action to avert collision. Its sole purpose is to give a power-driven vessel which is required to hold her course and speed the opportunity of calling the attention of the burdened vessel to its obligations under the International Rules to keep clear. This differentiation between the two danger signals is important, and must be understood, for each of these signals must be used in its proper manner and in its proper jurisdiction. There might be occasions when it would be highly desirable to use the Inland danger signal at sea, but you cannot legally do so. Under such circumstances you must use a signal authorized by the International Rules to attract attention, or else turn to the International Code of Signals. There are two especially useful one-letter warning signals in the latter:

(1) The letter U, which signifies "You are standing into danger";

(2) The letter D, which signifies "Keep clear of me, I am maneuvering with difficulty."

Either one of these signals can be transmitted visually, by means of Morse Code using flashing light, or by whistle or siren.

BEND SIGNALS

Under the Inland Rules, the bend signal is a doubly useful single long blast of 8 to 10 seconds' duration, which is required to be given by:

(1) A steam (i.e., power-driven) vessel approaching within half a mile of a blind bend or curve in a channel where a vessel approaching from the opposite direction cannot be seen for a distance of half a mile. In such instances, should the signal be answered, as is required, by a vessel around the bend, signals for meeting and passing should be given and answered *immediately upon sighting each other,* rather than upon hearing the answering signal.

(2) A steam (i.e., power-driven) vessel emerging from a slip, dock, or berth. Here the signal is not answer-

able, and until such time as the emerging vessel is clear and steadied on a course and speed, neither she nor an approaching vessel has a right of way. Thereupon, however, the Rules for meeting, crossing, and overtaking vessels apply.

Under International Rules, on the other hand, the bend signal is a single purpose signal consisting of a prolonged blast of 4 to 6 seconds duration, which is required to be given by a power-driven (i.e., steam) vessel within one-half mile of a blind bend or curve in a channel where a vessel approaching from the other direction cannot be seen for any distance. It must answered by a power-driven vessel within hearing distance around the bend, but subsequent signals are given only if either vessel has to change course.

FOG SIGNALS There are numerous differences in sound signals prescribed under International and Inland Rules for vessels in fog or other conditions of similarly restricted visibility. Under both sets of Rules, however, all vessels are required to give notice of their position by signals on the whistle, siren, fog horn, bell, or gong at prescribed *maximum* intervals, when *in* or *about* areas of restricted visibility. Therefore, you must know what the differences are, what signals apply where, and at what intervals the specific signals are to be given. There is no guidance in the Rules as to the distance a fog signal must be audible or the maximum visibility that requires its use; and the courts have not been much more specific on either point. But, even in the absence of positive limits, you will nevertheless generally be wise to sound appropriate fog signals when visibility has decreased to 1 to 2 miles, and, if underway, to decrease speed proportionately.

NOT UNDER COMMAND SIGNALS

A disabled vessel which is unable to comply with the meeting and passing Rules must apprise approaching vessels of her plight. Outside inland waters, this condition is indicated by the use of two black balls or shapes by day, two all-around red lights at night, and whistle signals of one-prolonged-and-two-short blasts when under way in restricted visibility. In inland waters, where these signals have other meanings, inability to comply with the meeting and passing Rules is indicated by a timely use of the Inland danger signal.

DISTRESS SIGNALS

Technically speaking, the distress signals prescribed by the International Rules cannot be used in inland waters. However, the majority of them have the force of custom in inland waters, and therefore may be used in those waters when it is necessary to do so.

SOME USEFUL AXIOMS

TIMELY AND POSITIVE ACTION In obeying and construing the Rules of the Road, any action taken should be positive, in ample time, and with due regard to the observance of good seamanship.

AIRCRAFT CARRIERS An aircraft carrier, while operating aircraft, has the right of way over all other *naval* vessels, regardless of their size, type, or description. Other naval vessels must stay clear of that carrier, and if it is necessary to pass her when she is operating aircraft, the following rules apply:

(1) If the carrier is headed into the wind, pass on her starboard side;

(2) If the carrier is headed out of the wind, pass on her lee side.

MINESWEEPERS A minesweeper engaged in sweeping (i.e., with sweeps out) may be passed no closer than 500 yards on either beam or 1000 yards astern.

SMALL VESSELS A small vessel should not hamper the movements of a larger vessel, especially in restricted waters.

VESSELS NOT IN STATION Vessels which are not in station should not hamper those in station. On the other hand, vessels in station should not stubbornly maintain their course and speed if danger of collision exists.

FORMATION VS. SINGLE VESSEL Normally, a vessel proceeding independently should maneuver to stay clear of a formation. Merchant vessels, however, will often maintain their right of way and run directly into a formation. Under favorable circumstances, in good visibility when no other naval vessels are involved, the commander of a small formation will probably maneuver his unit to clear the "outsider." But the Officer of the Deck of a vessel in formation can not, and should not, count on the unit being maneuvered clear. This is a difficult, if not impossible, maneuver under many conditions. Under all circumstances, the Officer of the Deck is responsible for handling his own vessel in accordance with the applicable Rules of the Road in regard to the "outsider," and in accordance with standard naval instructions in regard to naval vessels in formation.

LIGHT DISPLAYS, DAYMARKS, AND SOUND SIGNALS

For easy reference, light displays, daymarks, and sound signals are listed in the following pages in the order mentioned, first for International Rules, and then in the same order for Inland Rules. The colored plates that complete the presentation in this part of the Chapter show some common light displays under both International and Inland Rules.

The characteristics of the individual lights are given by letters, numerals, or words which denote: first, color; second, arc of visibility in points (11¼ degrees); third, range of visibility in miles.

Bear in mind throughout that, under International Rules, lights prescribed for seaplanes on the water are similar to those prescribed for vessels in a given situation; and that a seaplane on the high seas must conform to the Steering and Sailing Rules applicable to power-driven vessels; while the Inland Rules are silent as to waterborne seaplanes in inland waters.

LIGHT DISPLAYS

[International]

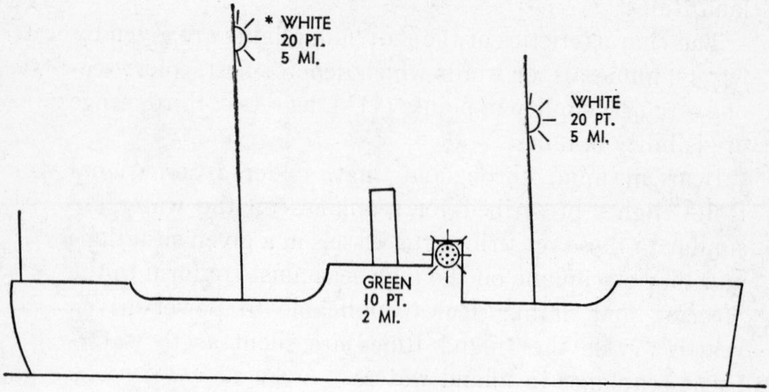

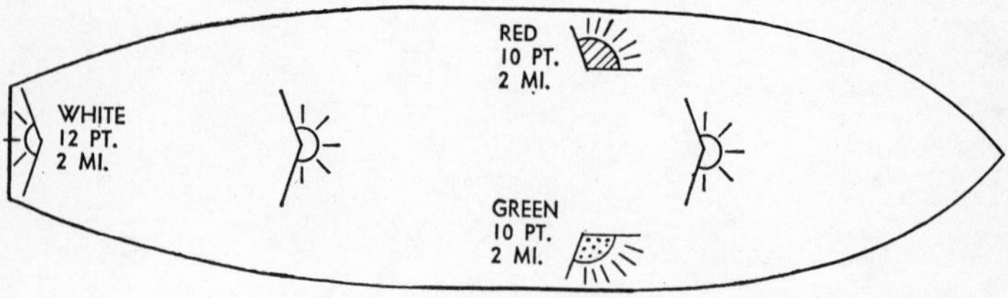

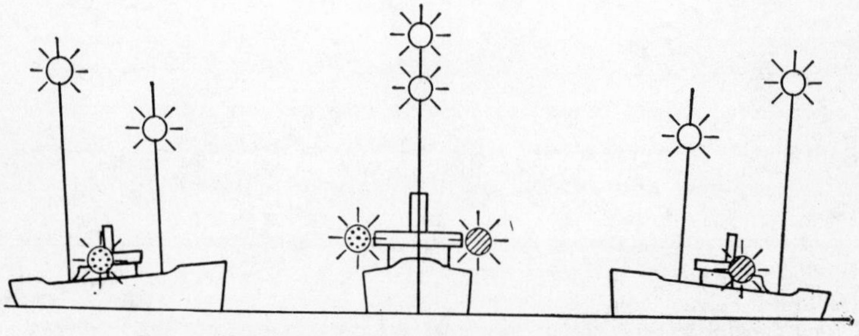

Power-driven vessel under way. [International.]

** Optional if less than 150 feet in length.*

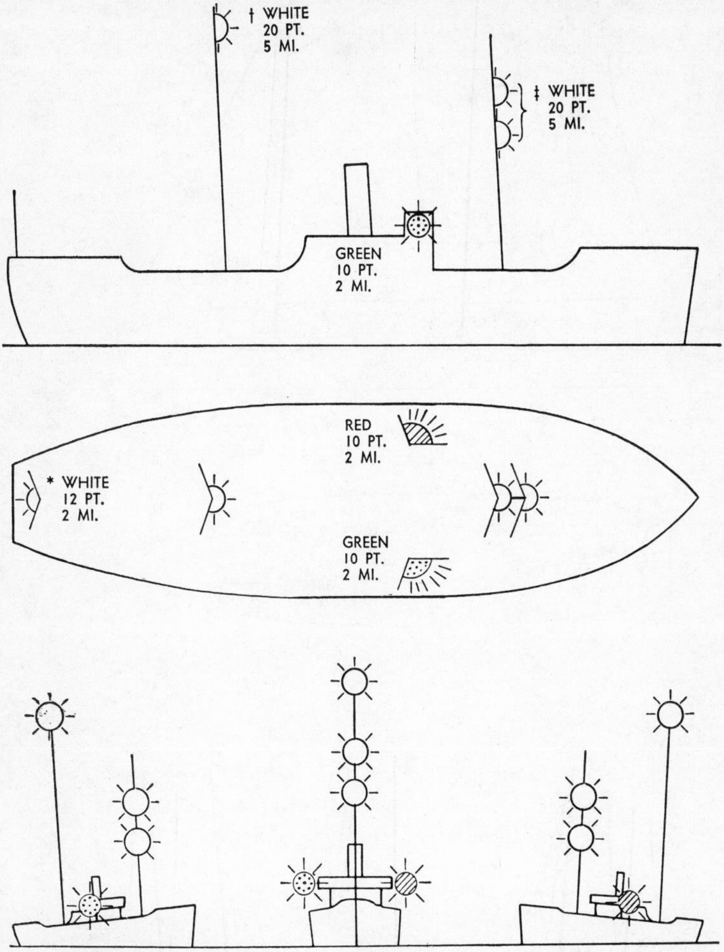

Power-driven vessel towing or pushing one or more vessels or seaplanes, except when a tow astern consists of two or more vessels or seaplanes and exceeds 600 feet in length. [International.]

***** *Vessel may show a steering light that is not visible forward of the beam in lieu of the fixed stern light when the tow is astern.*

† ***Optional.***

‡ ***When two or more vessels or seaplanes are towed astern and the length of the tow, measured from the stern of the towing vessel to the stern of the last vessel or seaplane towed, is more than 600 feet, an additional light is shown on the foremast.***

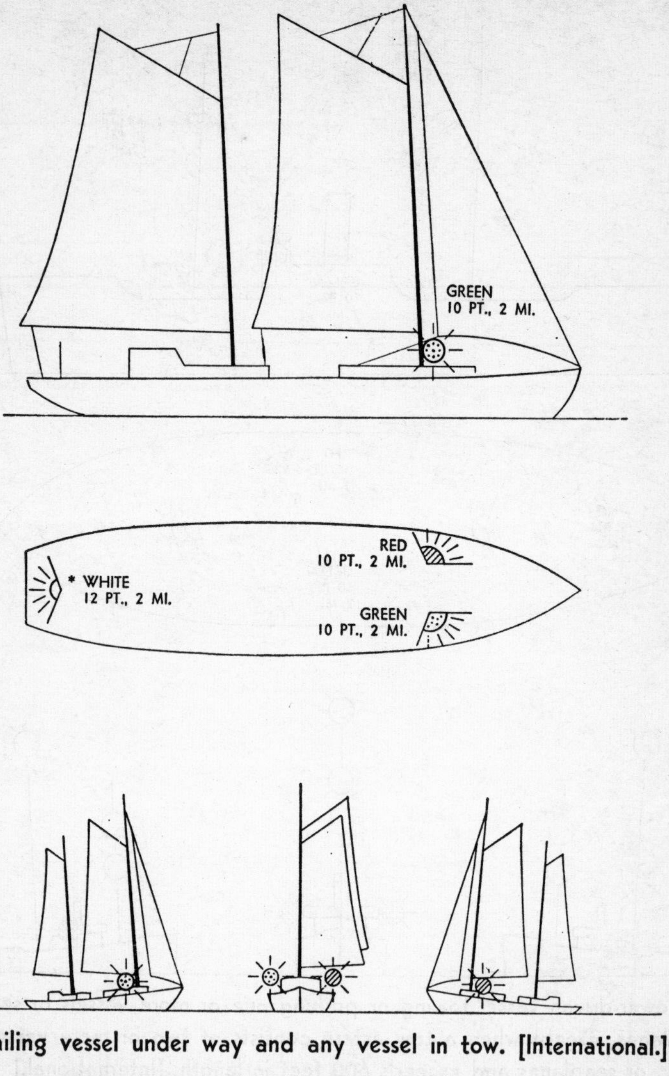

Sailing vessel under way and any vessel in tow. [International.]†

***** *Except when she is the last vessel of a tow, a vessel towed astern is allowed to carry a small steering light that is not visible forward of the beam in lieu of the fixed stern light.*

† A seaplane in tow carries the same lights rounded off to the nearest ten degrees of arc of visibility. One or more vessels being pushed ahead are lighted as one vessel and carry only the sidelights shown above, at the forward end.

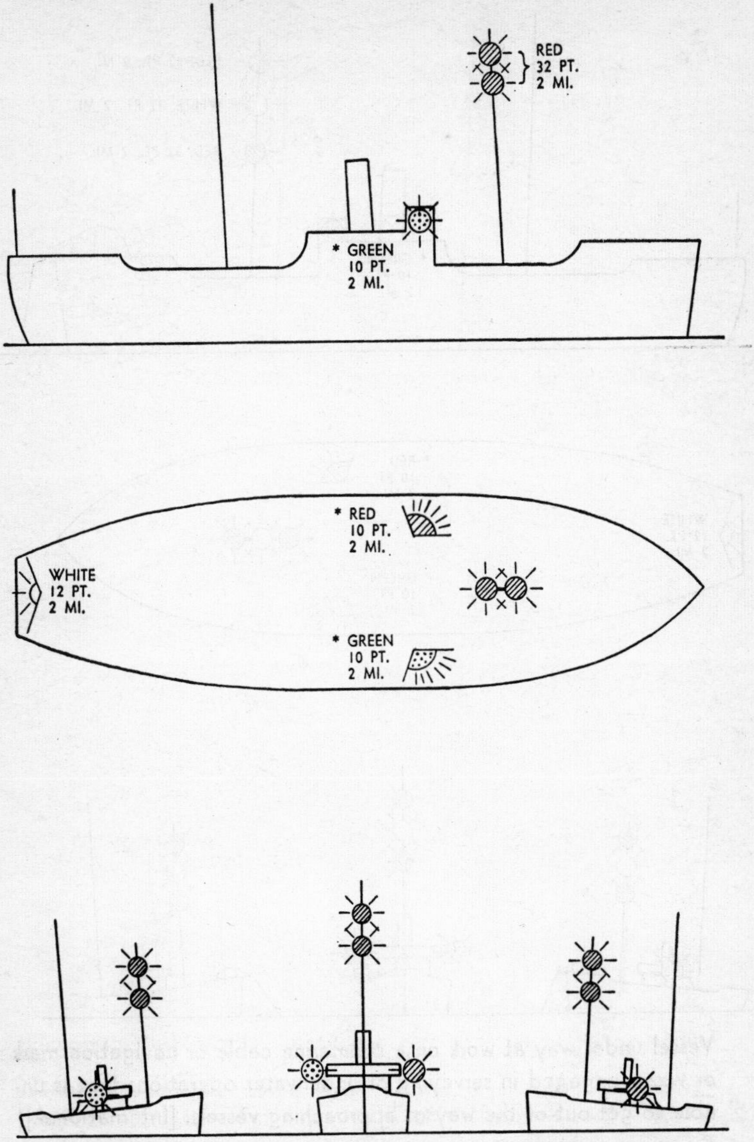

Vessel under way and not under command. [International.]

***** *Sidelights are shown only when making way.*

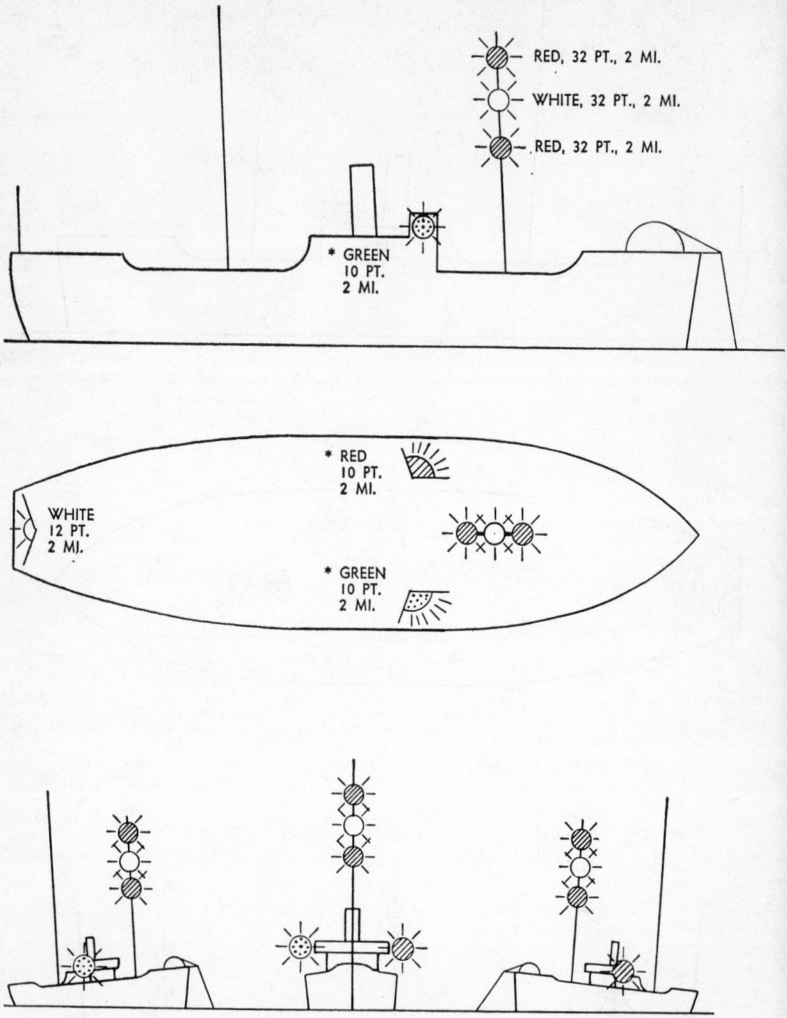

Vessel under way at work on a submarine cable or navigation mark or vessel engaged in surveying or underwater operations that is unable to get out of the way of approaching vessels. [International.]†

** Sidelights are shown only when making way.*

† When at anchor and engaged in the occupations indicated, these vessels show the red-white-red lights and anchor lights.

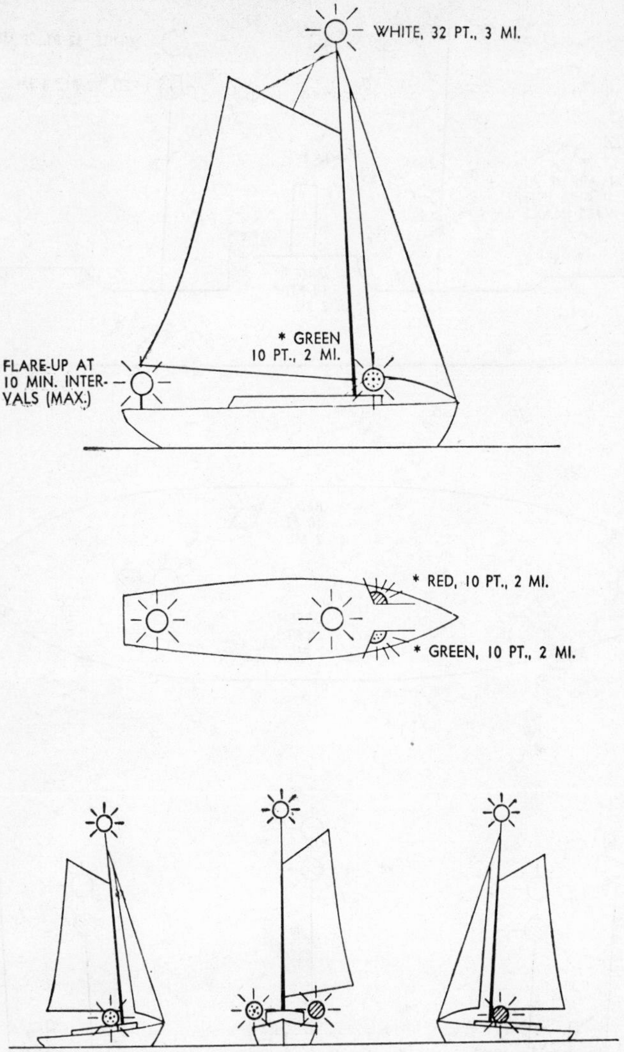

Sailing pilot-vessel under way on station on pilotage duty. [International.]†

Sidelights are flashed at short intervals on near approach of or to another vessel.

† When on station on pilotage duty and at anchor, a sailing pilot-vessel exhibits the white light and flare shown above and anchor lights for her class.

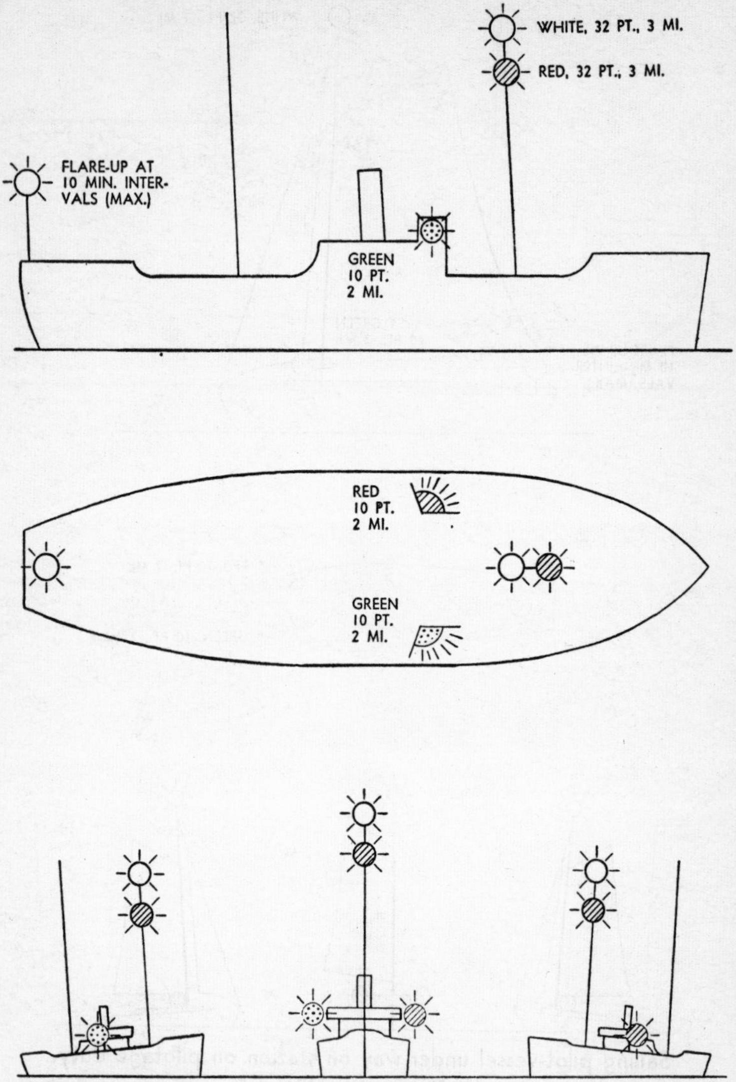

Power-driven pilot-vessel under way on station on pilotage duty. [International.]†

† When on station on pilotage duty and at anchor, a power-driven pilot-vessel exhibits the masthead lights and flare shown above and anchor lights for her class.

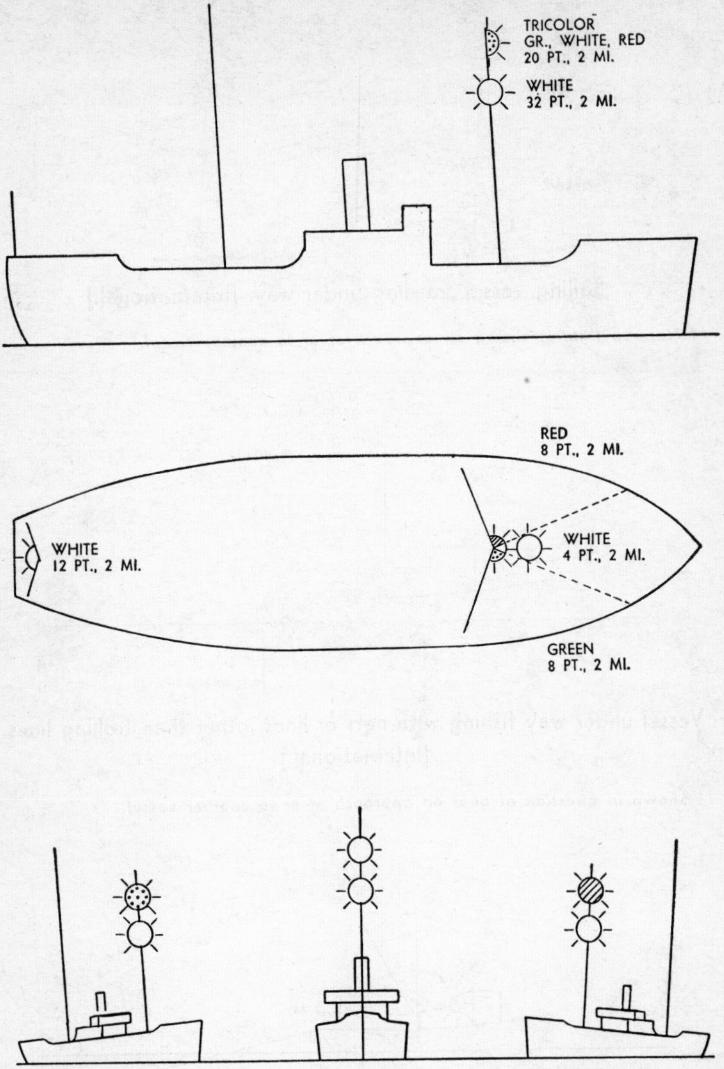

Power-driven vessel trawling under way. [International].†

† When trawling at anchor, a power-driven trawler exhibits anchor lights for her class, and on the approach of another vessel shows an additional white light below and away from the forward anchor light, in the direction of her outlying gear, as does every vessel fishing at anchor, regardless of the type of fishing engaged in or the nature of the vessel fishing.

Sailing vessel trawling under way. [International.]

*** Flare-up light is shown on approach of or to another vessel.**

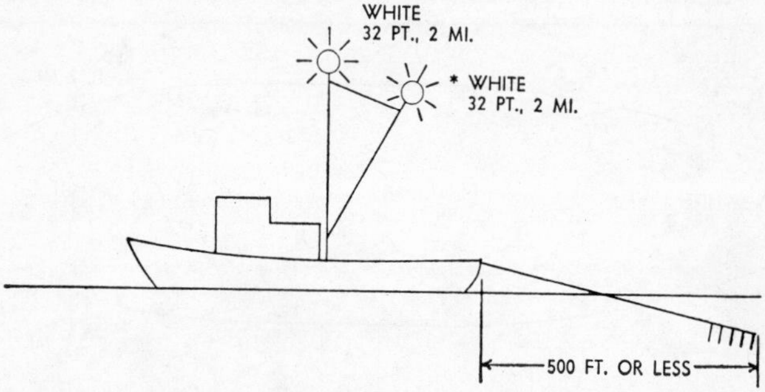

Vessel under way fishing with nets or lines, other than trolling lines. [International.]

*** Shown in direction of gear on approach of or to another vessel.**

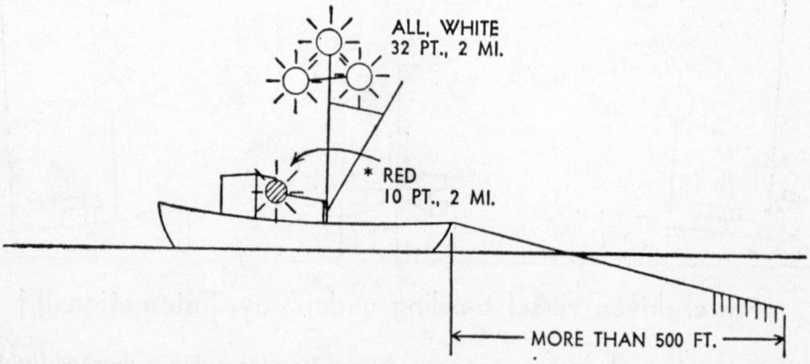

Vessel under way fishing with nets or lines, other than trolling lines. [International.]

*** Sidelights are shown only when making way.**

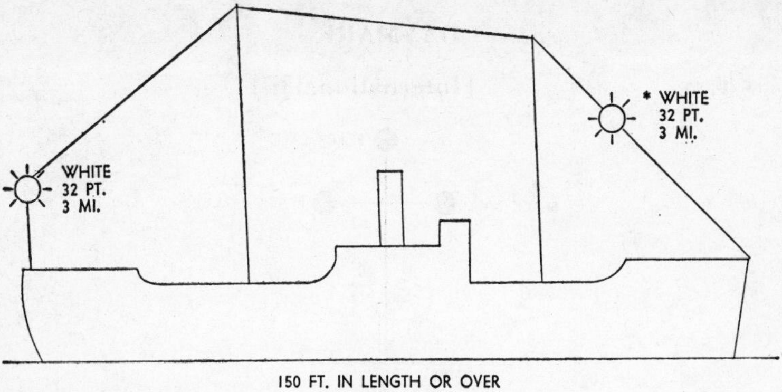

Vessel at anchor. [International.]

A vessel under 150 feet in length shows a white, 32 pt., 2 mi. light in place of the forward light, where it can best be seen, and no after light.

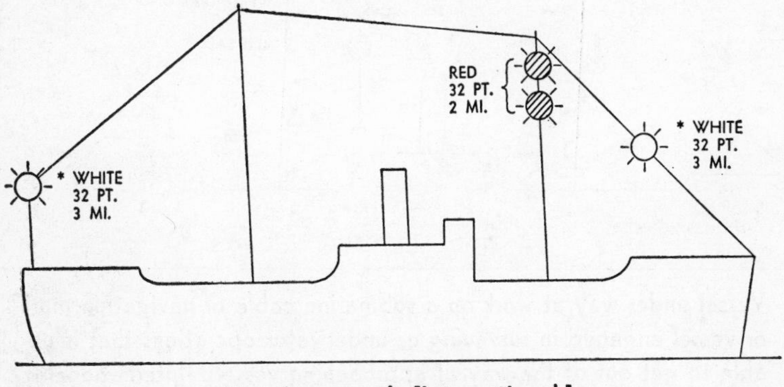

Vessel aground. [International.]

Shows the anchor lights for a vessel of her class (see plate above).

DAYMARKS

[International]

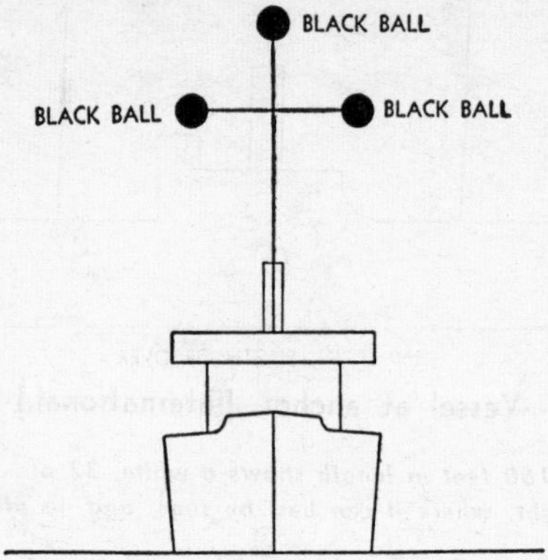

Minesweeper engaged in sweeping. [International.]†

† May and customarily does carry black balls at the masthead and on the yardarm(s), but, if she is unable to get out of way of approaching vessels, must carry three shapes in a vertical line, of which the highest and lowest is globular in shape and red in color, and the middle one diamond in shape and white (see plate below).

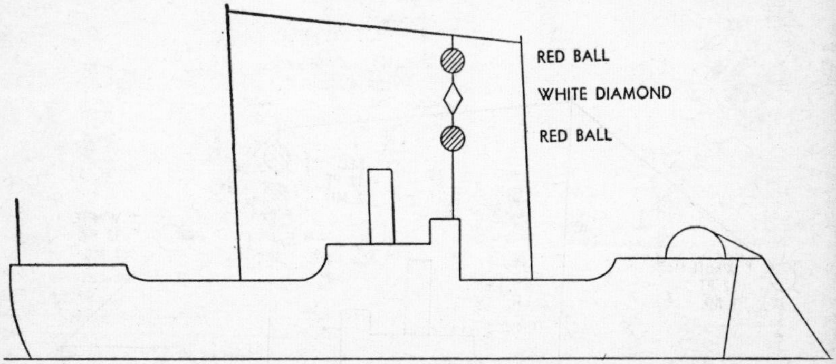

Vessel under way at work on a submarine cable or navigation mark or vessel engaged in surveying or underwater operations that is unable to get out of the way of approaching vessels. [International.]†

† When at anchor and engaged in the operations indicated, these vessels show an anchor ball in addition to the red-white-red shapes.

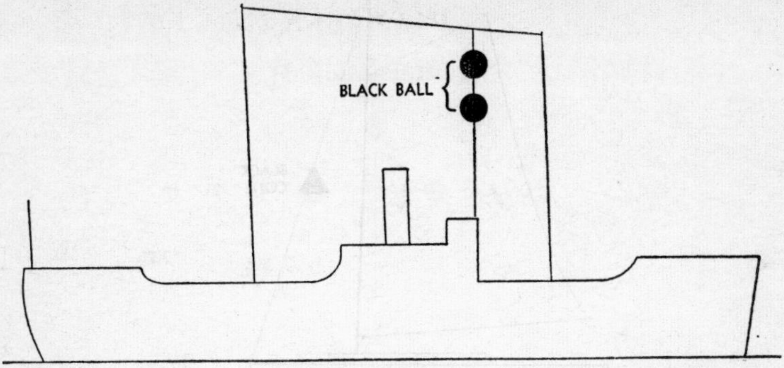

Vessel under way and not under command. [International.]

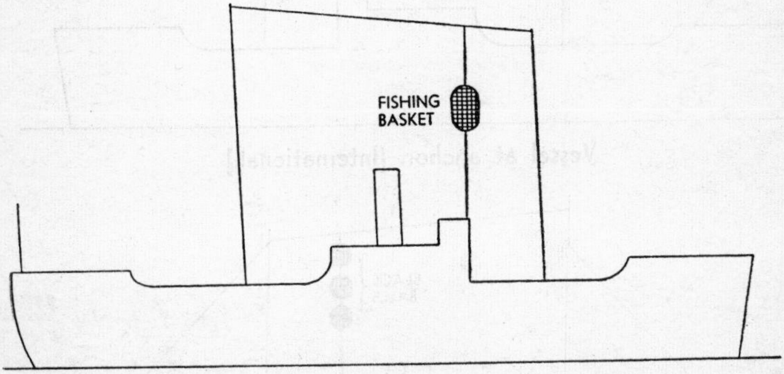

Vessel fishing under way. [International.]† ‡

† A vessel fishing under way with gear, other than trolling lines, extending over 500 feet horizontally into the seaway must also show a black conical shape, apex upwards, where it can best be seen.

‡ When fishing at anchor, the basket is shown in the direction from the anchor ball towards the net or gear.

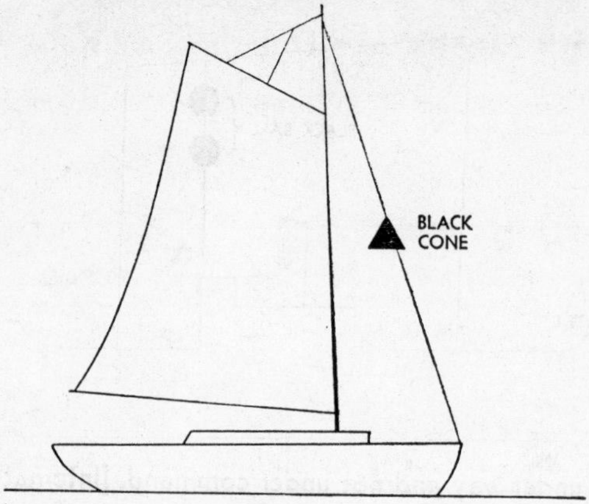

Vessel under sail and power. [International.]

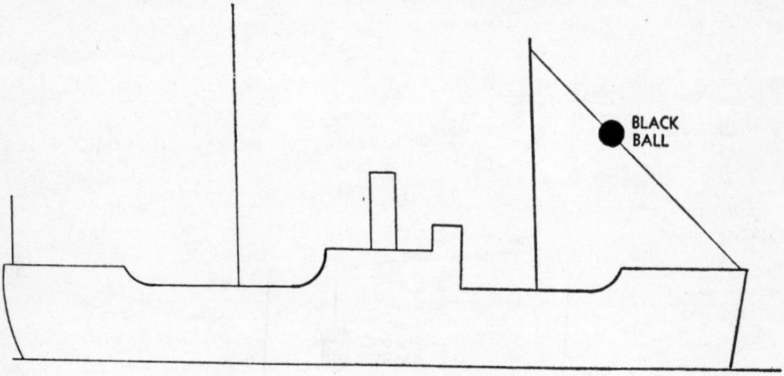

Vessel at anchor. [International.]

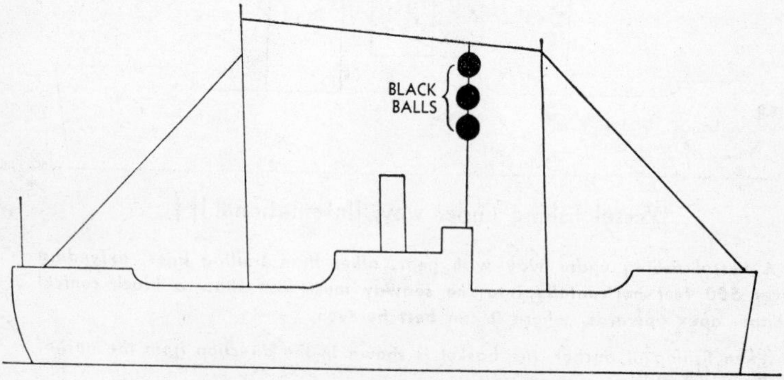

Vessel aground. [International.]

SOUND SIGNALS [International Rules.]

The following symbols are used to indicate sound signals of different lengths:

-	a short blast (about one second duration)
—	a blast of unspecified duration
——	a prolonged blast (four to six seconds duration)
*	three separate and distinct taps on a bell
*****	ringing of a bell
.....	sounding of a gong

Sound signals for power-driven vessels in sight of each other

Signal	*Instrument*	*Meaning*
-	Whistle or siren	I am directing my course to starboard
- -	Whistle or siren	I am directing my course to port
- - -	Whistle or siren	My engines are backing *or* I have sternway on
- - - - - (or more)	Whistle or siren	Danger, keep clear; I am privileged
——	Whistle or siren	I am within ½ mile of the blind bend, *or* I acknowledge your signal

Sound signals given when visibility is restricted

Type of vessel	*Instrument*	*Signal*	*Maximum Interval*
Power-driven vessel under way with way upon her	Whistle or siren	——	2 minutes
Power-driven vessel under way but stopped and having no way upon her	Whistle or siren	—— ——	2 minutes
Vessel towing			
Power-driven vessel	Whistle or siren	—— - -	1 minute
Sailing vessel	Foghorn	—— - -	1 minute
Last vessel being towed	Whistle, siren, or foghorn	—— - - - (If manned)	1 minute

Type of vessel	Instrument	Signal	Maximum Interval
Vessel under way and not under command			
Power-driven vessel	Whistle or siren	——— – –	1 minute
Sailing vessel	Foghorn	——— – –	1 minute
Vessel working with submarine cable or navigation mark			
Power-driven vessel	Whistle or siren	——— – –	1 minute
Sailing vessel	Foghorn	——— – –	1 minute
Vessel at anchor			
All vessels	Bell	*****	1 minute
Over 350 ft.	Gong	.....	After bell
Vessel aground			
350 ft. or less	Bell	* ***** *	1 minute
Over 350 ft.	Bell and Gong	* ***** ..... *	1 minute
Collision warning			
At anchor or aground	Sail, foghorn; others, whistle or siren	– ——— – (Optional)	None
Sailing vessels			
On starboard tack	Foghorn	—	1 minute
On port tack	Foghorn	— —	1 minute
Wind abaft the beam	Foghorn	— — —	1 minute
Vessels 20 tons or over, fishing			
Power-driven vessel	Whistle or siren and bell	— *****	1 minute
Sailing vessel	Foghorn and bell	— *****	1 minute

Note: Vessels under 20 gross tons, rowing boats, and seaplanes may give the above signals, but need only make some efficient sound signal at intervals of not more than 1 minute.

LIGHT DISPLAYS

[Inland]

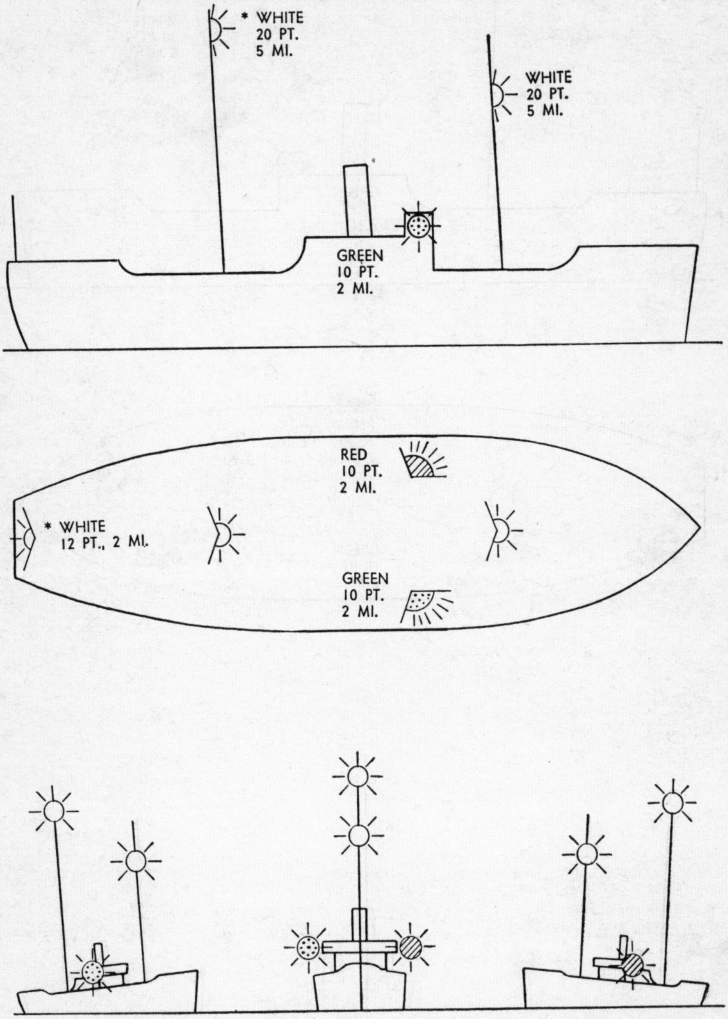

Seagoing steam vessel under way. [Inland.]

**** Irrespective of their optional nature under the Inland Rules, these two lights will be shown in inland waters, as they are specifically required under the International Rules.***

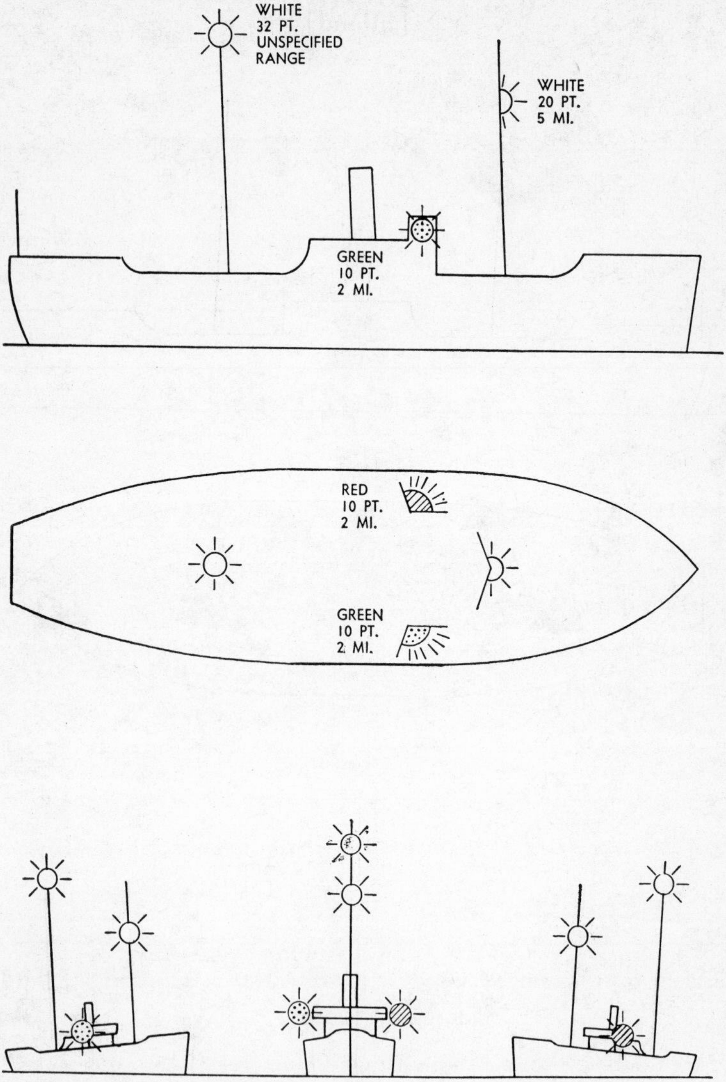

Non-seagoing steam vessel under way. [Inland.]

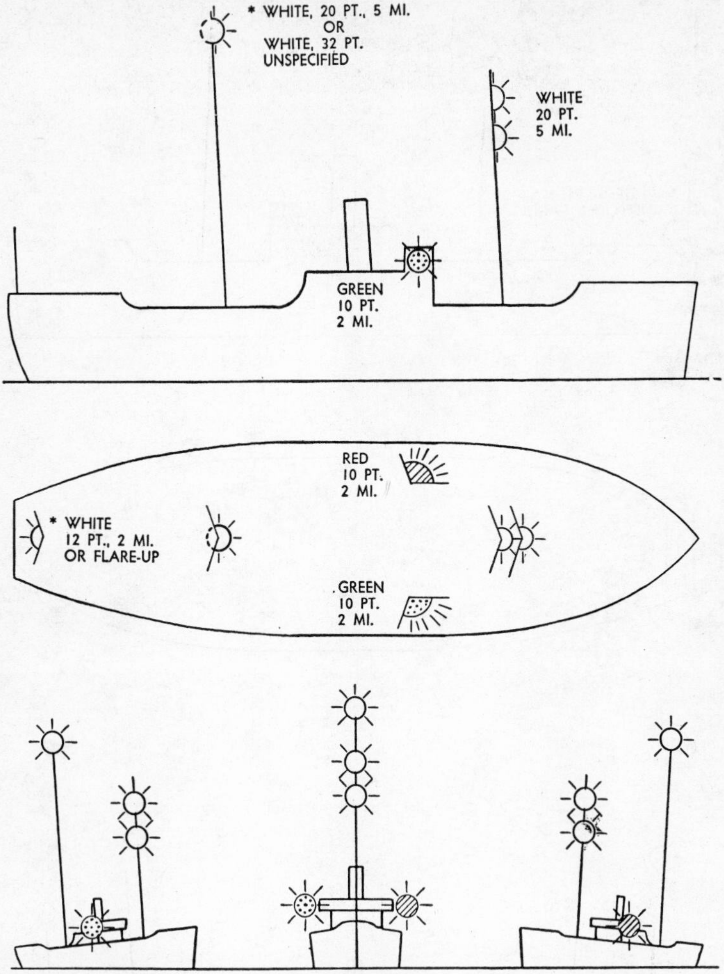

Steam vessel towing alongside <u>or</u> pushing ahead with towing lights forward. [Inland.]†

**** The fixed stern light and the after range light are both optional. With towing lights forward, it is only necessary to show a white light or a flare-up light to an overtaking vessel when being overtaken. If carried, a seagoing steam vessel shows her 20-point after range light and her fixed stern light, while a non-seagoing steam vessel shows her 32-point after range light.***

† In lieu of the white lights shown above, a steam vessel towing alongside or by pushing ahead may carry two 32-point white lights aft.

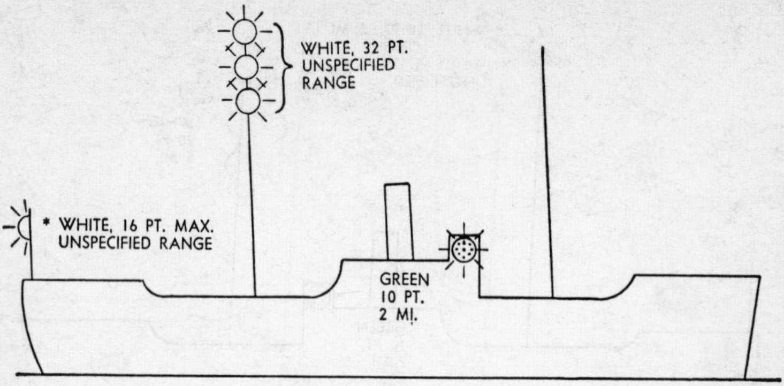

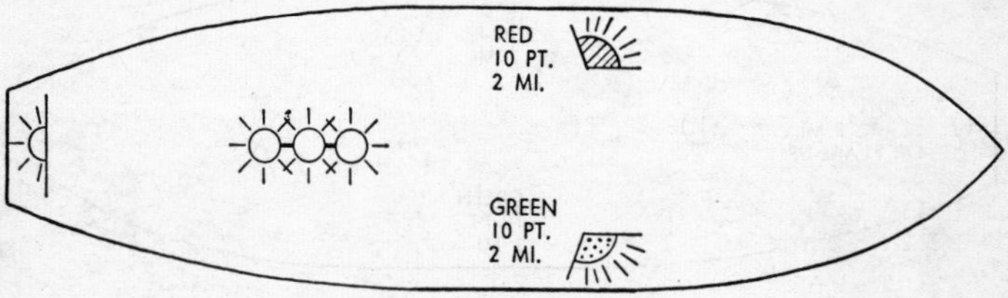

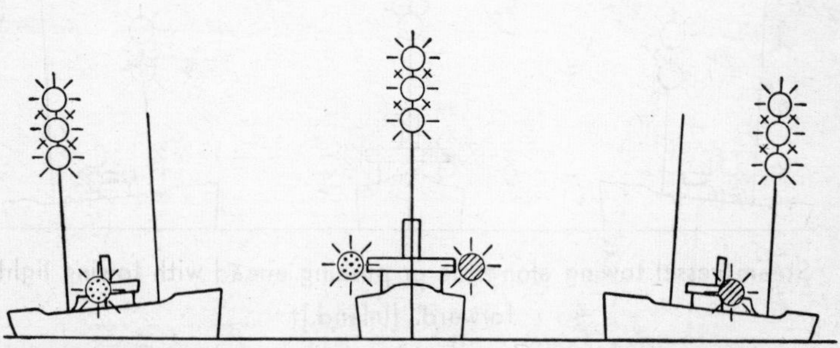

Steam vessel towing astern with towing lights aft. [Inland.]†

**** Optional steering light. Cannot show forward of the beam.***

† Three white, 20-point, 5 mile lights may be shown forward in lieu of the three 32-point lights shown above. Whereupon, the towing vessel may, at her option, also carry an after range light.

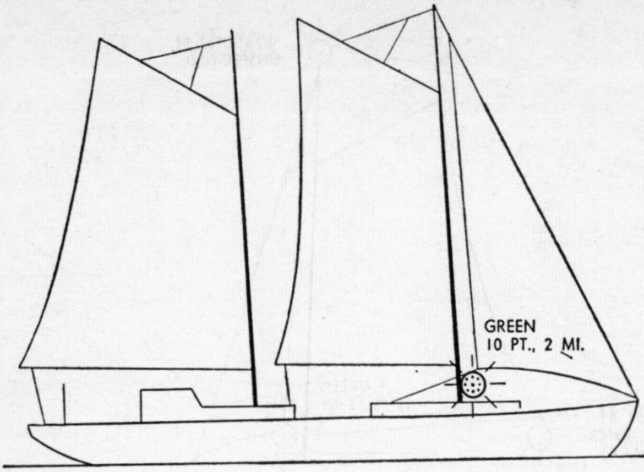

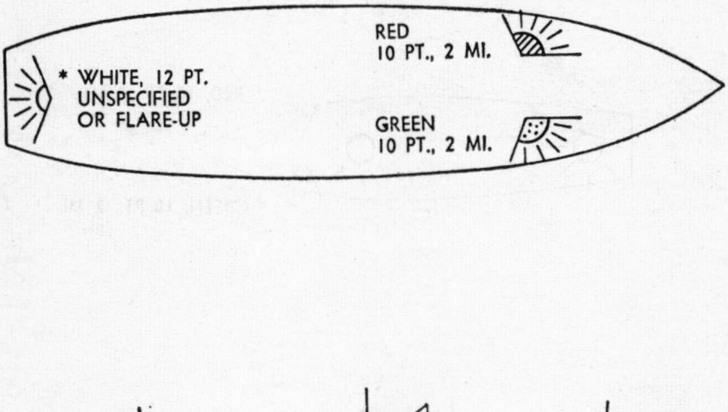

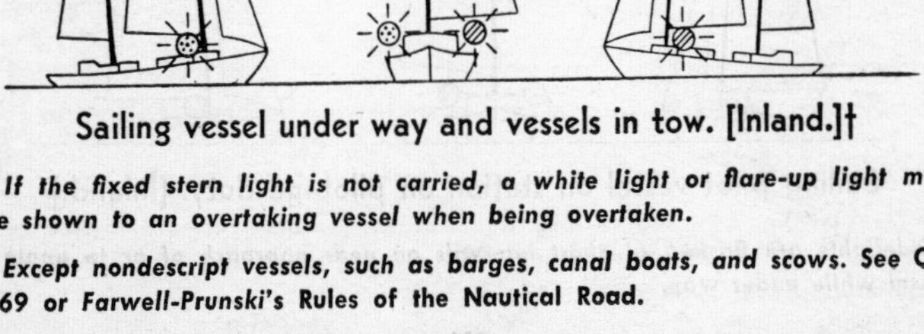

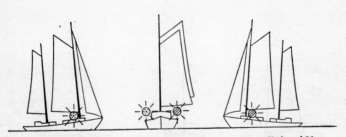

Sailing vessel under way and vessels in tow. [Inland.]†

**** If the fixed stern light is not carried, a white light or flare-up light must be shown to an overtaking vessel when being overtaken.***

† Except nondescript vessels, such as barges, canal boats, and scows. See CG-169 or Farwell-Prunski's Rules of the Nautical Road.

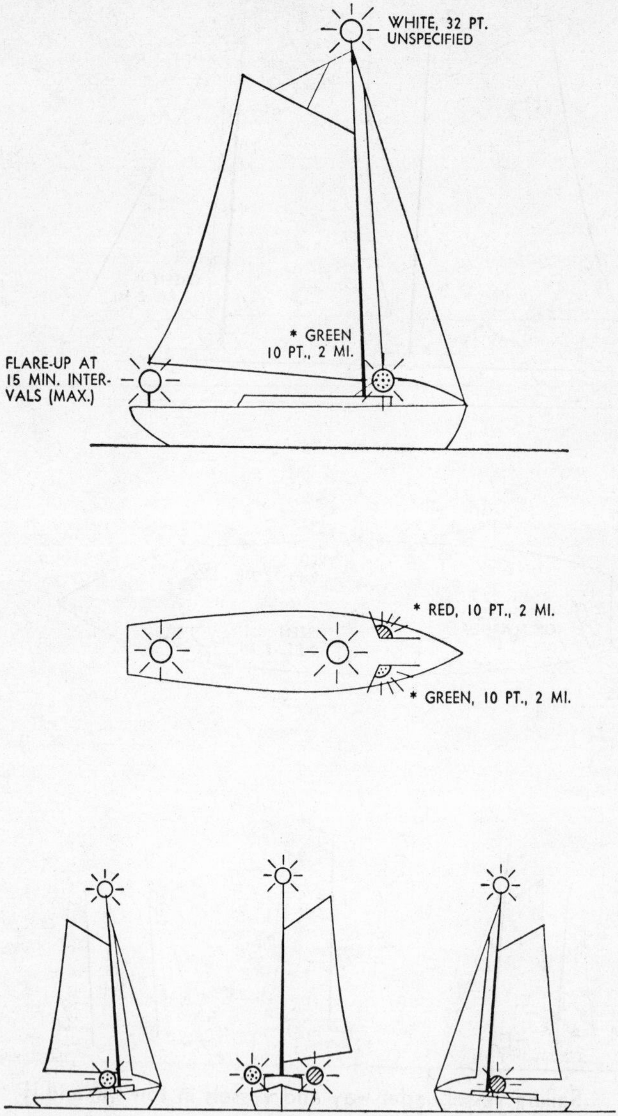

Sailing pilot vessel on station on pilotage duty. [Inland.]

**** Sidelights are flashed at short intervals on near approach of or to another vessel while under way.***

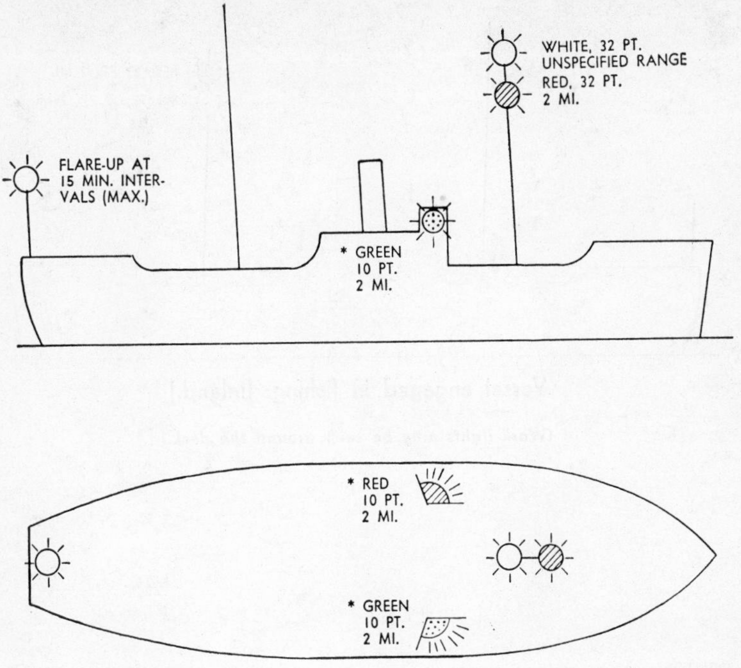

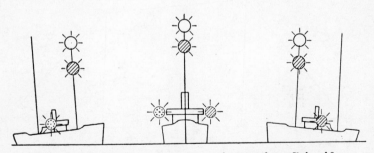

Steam pilot vessel on station on pilotage duty. [Inland.]

**** Sidelights are shown only when under way.***

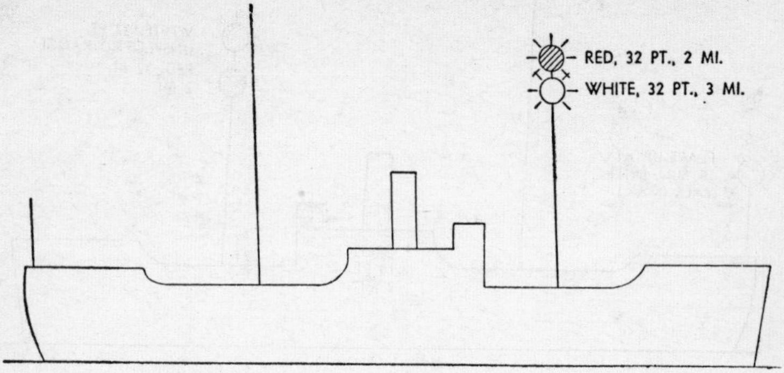

Vessel engaged in fishing. [Inland.]

(Work lights may be seen around the deck.)

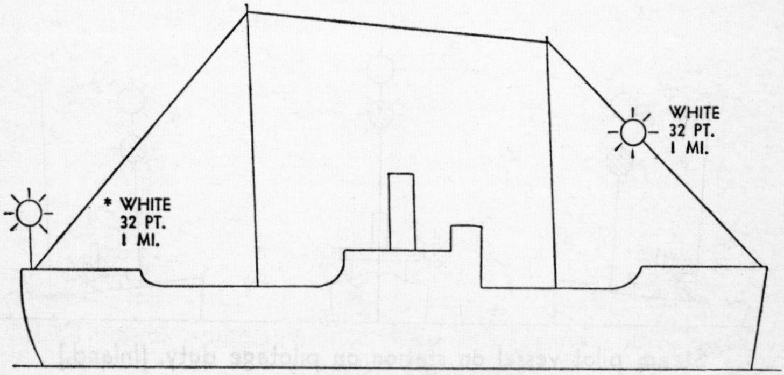

150 FT. IN LENGTH OR OVER

Vessel at anchor. [Inland.]

A vessel under 150 feet in length does not show the after light.

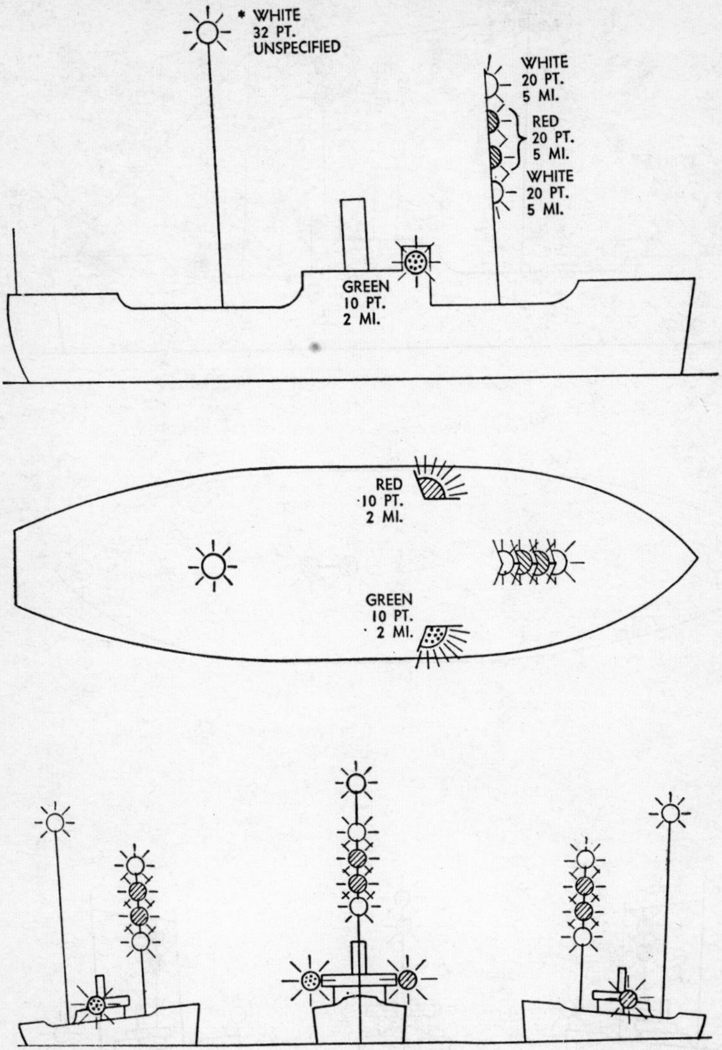

Vessel with submerged or partly submerged tow, towing lights forward. [Inland.]†

**** Optional.***

† In lieu of the 20-point lights shown above, similarly arranged and colored 32-point lights may be shown aft.

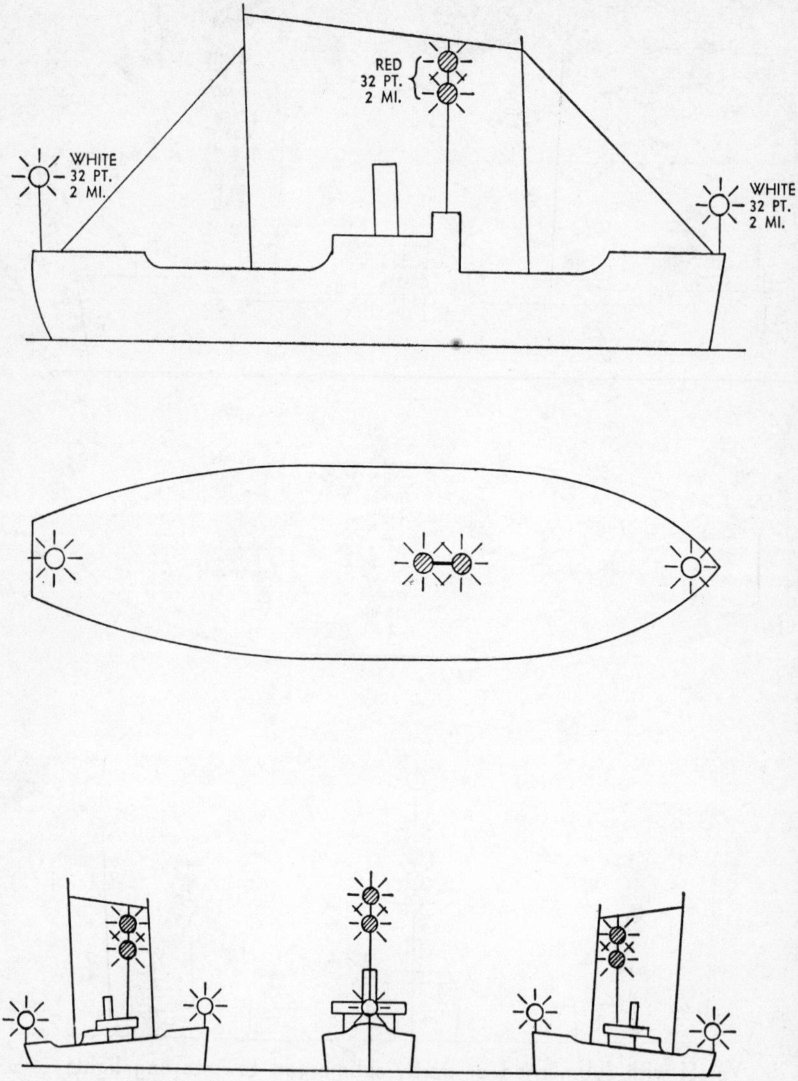

Vessel moored alongside or over a wreck. [Inland.]†

† Two red, 32-point lights in a vertical line are also shown on: a stationary dredge; the open, shore, or discharge end of a pipe line attached to a dredge; a hydrographic survey vessel surveying at anchor; and a Coast Guard buoy tender working on an aid to navigation.

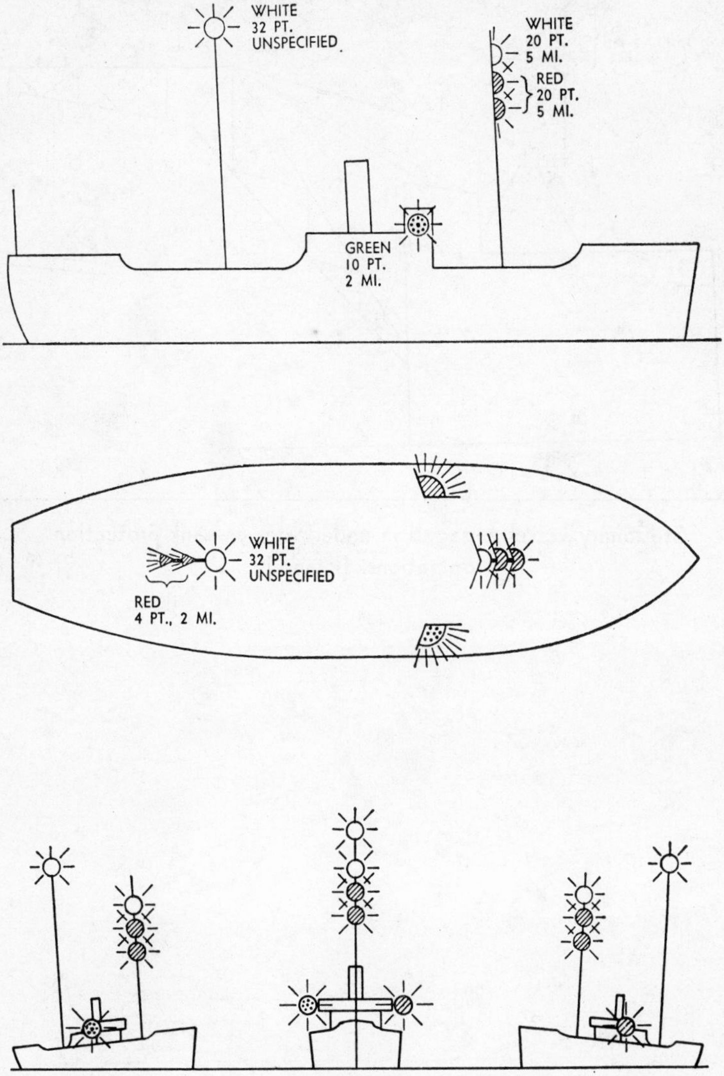

Self propelling suction dredge under way with suction down.
[Inland.]

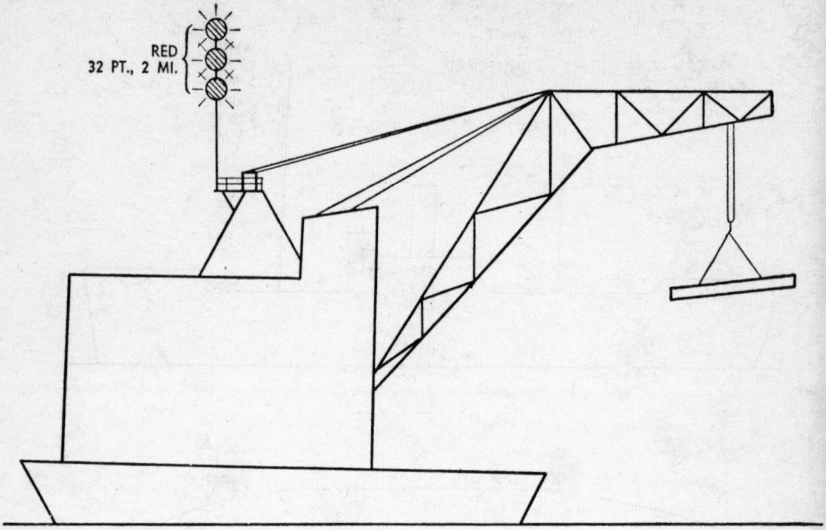

Stationary vessel engaged in underwater or bank protection operations. [Inland.]

DAYMARKS

[Inland]

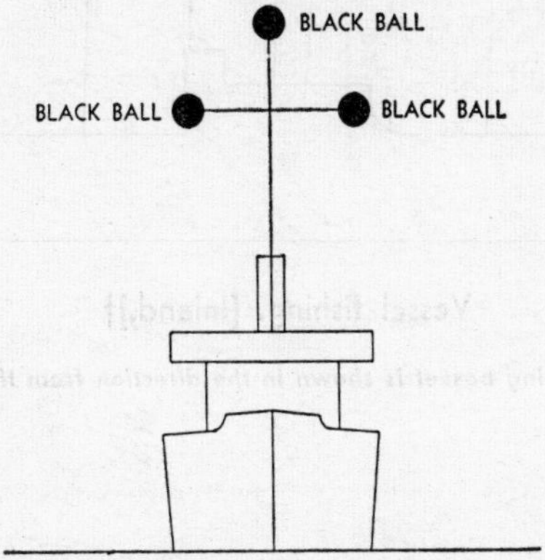

Minesweeper engaged in sweeping. [Inland.]†

† *Carries black balls at the masthead and on yardarm(s).*

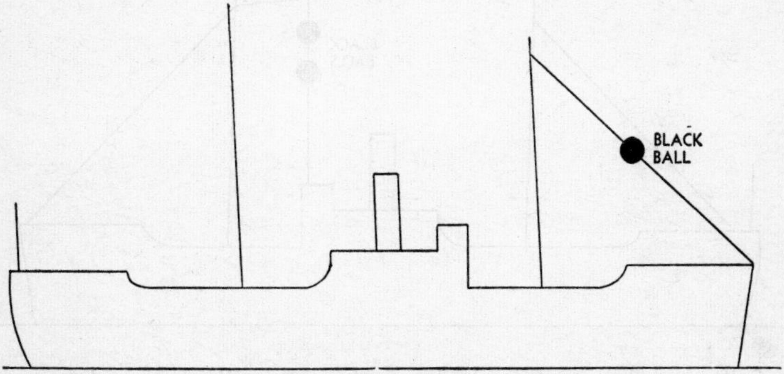

Vessel over 65 feet at anchor. [Inland.]

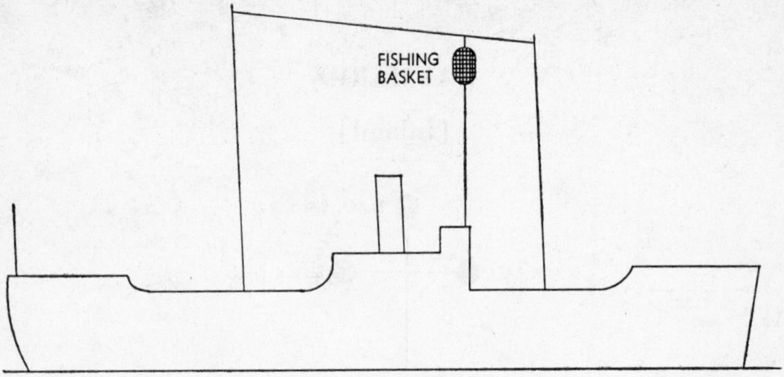

Vessel fishing. [Inland.]†

† ***At anchor the fishing basket is shown in the direction from the anchor towards the nets or gear.***

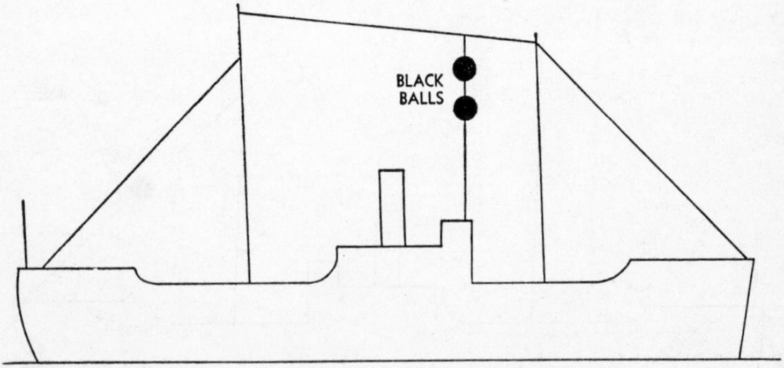

Self propelling suction dredge under way with suction down or hydrographic survey vessel surveying at anchor. [Inland.]

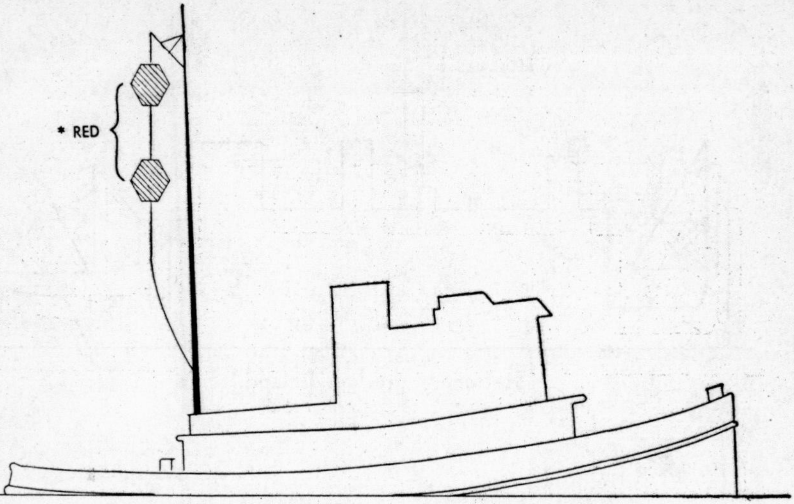

Vessel moored alongside or over a wreck. [Inland.]

*** Each a double frustum of a cone.***

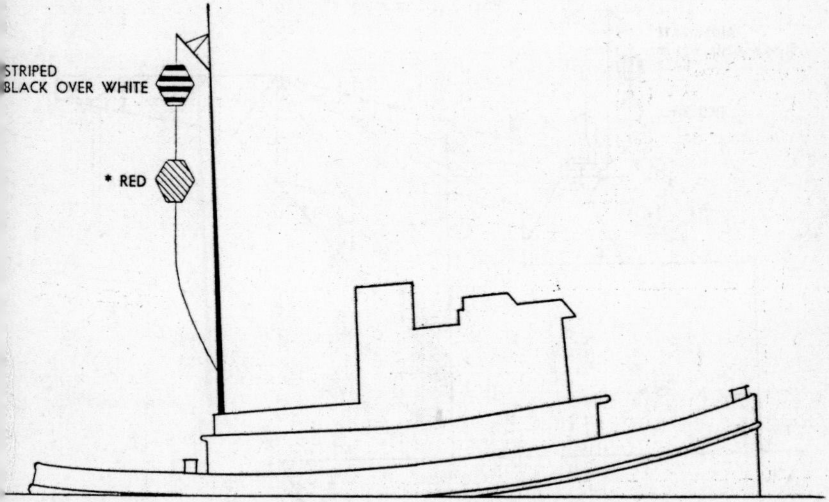

Vessel with submerged or partly submerged tow. [Inland.]

*** Double frustum of a cone.***

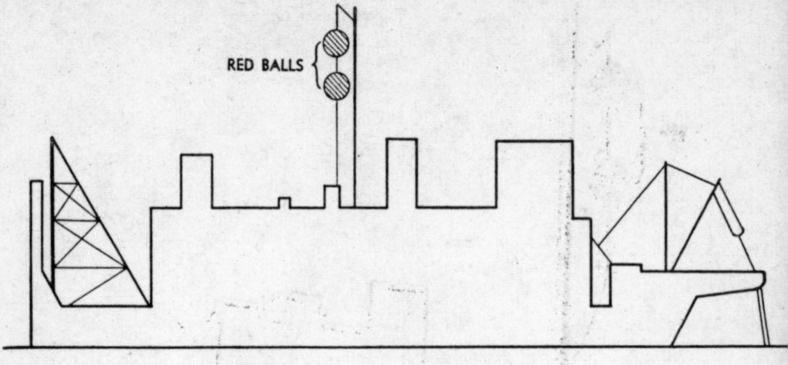

Stationary dredge. [Inland.]

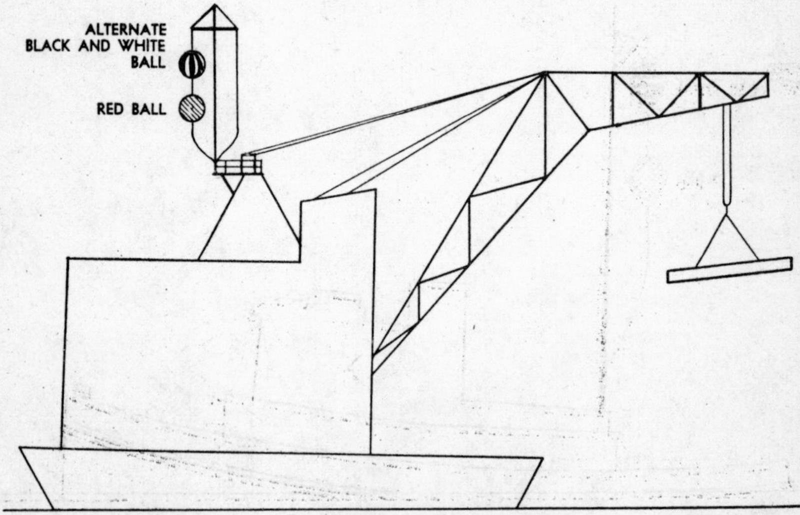

Stationary vessel engaged in underwater or bank protection operations. [Inland.]

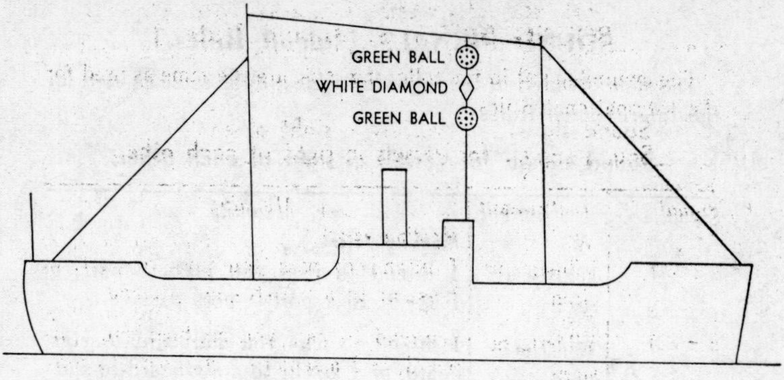

Hydrographic survey vessel surveying under way. [Inland.]

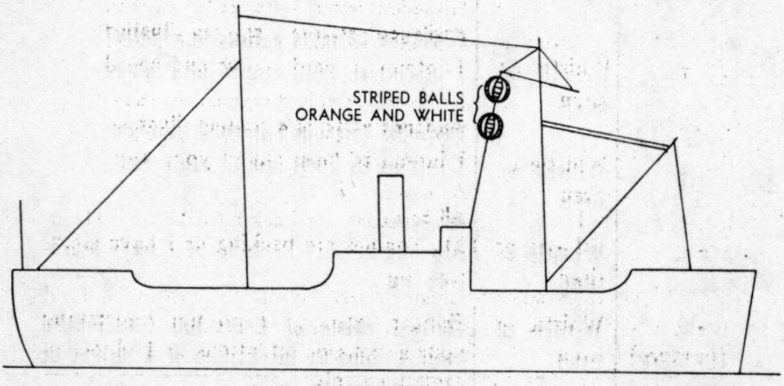

Coast Guard Tender servicing an aid to navigation. [Inland.]

SOUND SIGNALS [Inland Rules.]

The symbols used in the following table are the same as used for the International Rules.

Sound signals for vessels in sight of each other.

Signal	*Instrument*	*Meaning*
		Meeting vessel
- †	Whistle or siren	I intend to pass you port to port, *or* I assent to a port-to-port passage
- - †	Whistle or siren	I intend to pass you starboard to starboard, *or* I assent to a starboard-to-starboard passage
		Overtaking vessel
-	Whistle or siren	I desire to pass on your starboard hand
- -	Whistle or siren	I desire to pass on your port hand
		Overtaken vessel
- †	Whistle or siren	I assent to your passing on my starboard hand
- - †	Whistle or siren	I assent to your passing on my port hand
- - - - (or more)	Whistle or siren	I do not assent to your passing as proposed
		Privileged vessel in a crossing situation
- †	Whistle or siren	I intend to hold course and speed
		Burdened vessel in a crossing situation
- †	Whistle or siren	I intend to keep out of your way
		All cases
- - -	Whistle or siren	My engines are backing *or* I have sternway on
- - - - (or more)	Whistle or siren	Danger exists *or* I do not understand your actions or intentions *or* I object or cannot comply

† Cross signals are prohibited.

SOUND SIGNALS [Inland Rules cont.]

Sound signals for steam vessels not in sight of each other

Signal	*Instrument*	*Meaning*
——— ‡	Whistle or siren	I am leaving a slip; *or* I am approaching from within ½ mile of the obscured bend in the channel; *or* I am around the bend and hear you
- - - - (or more)	Whistle or siren	Danger exists

Sound signals given when visibility is restricted

Type of vessel	*Instrument*	*Signal*	*Maximum Interval*
Steam vessel underway	Whistle or siren	——	1 minute
Steam vessel towing	Whistle or siren	—— - -	1 minute
Vessel being towed	Foghorn	—— - - (Optional)	1 minute
Vessel at anchor	Bell	*****	1 minute
Sailing vessels			
On starboard tack	Foghorn	—	1 minute
On port tack	Foghorn	— —	1 minute
Wind abaft the beam	Foghorn	— — —	1 minute

‡ Long blast. This signal is peculiar to the Inland Rules. While not defined therein, it is held to be of 8 to 10 seconds duration.

LIGHT DISPLAYS

Seagoing steam vessel without after range light. [Inland.] Power-driven vessel under 150 feet without after range light. [International.]

Power-driven (i.e., steam) vessel with a central range of lights. [International and Inland.]

Sailing vessel (or vessel being towed). [International and Inland.]

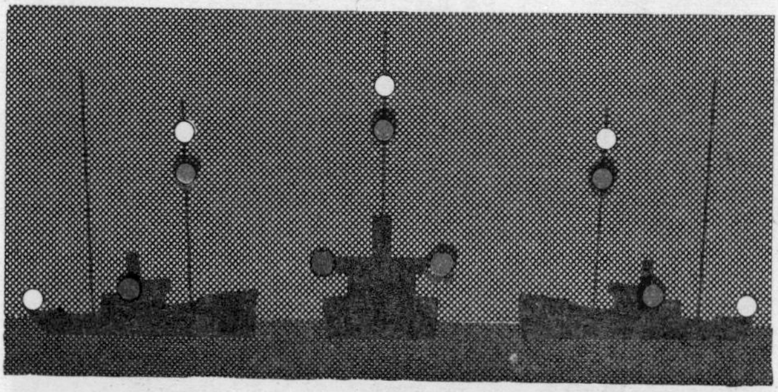

Power-driven (i.e., steam) pilot vessel under way on station on pilotage duty. [International and Inland.] (White light aft is flare-up.)

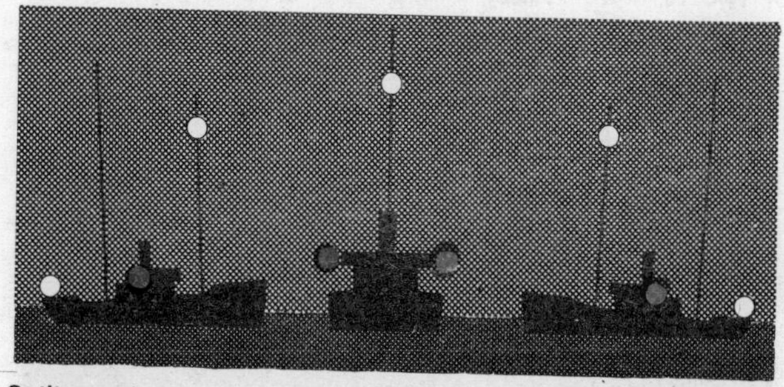

Sailing pilot vessel under way on station on pilotage duty with sidelights flashing. [International and Inland.] Sail omitted for clarity. White light aft is flare-up light.

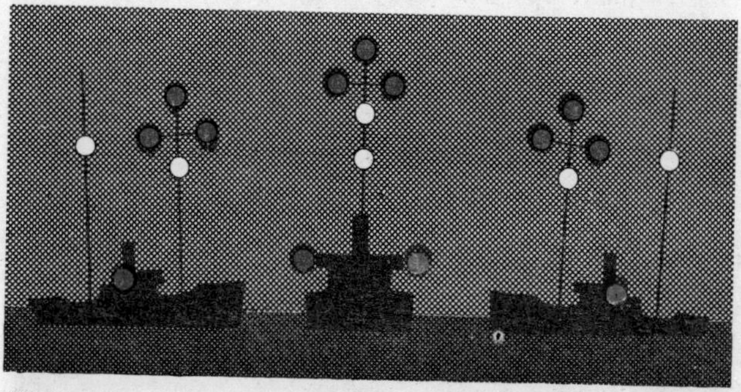

Minesweeper engaged in sweeping and able to maneuver (running lights plus additional lights). [International and Inland.]

Power-driven vessel with tow, except astern tow consisting of two or more vessels and exceeding 600 feet, showing optional after range light. [International.]

Steam vessel towing astern with towing lights forward but without optional after range light. [Inland.]

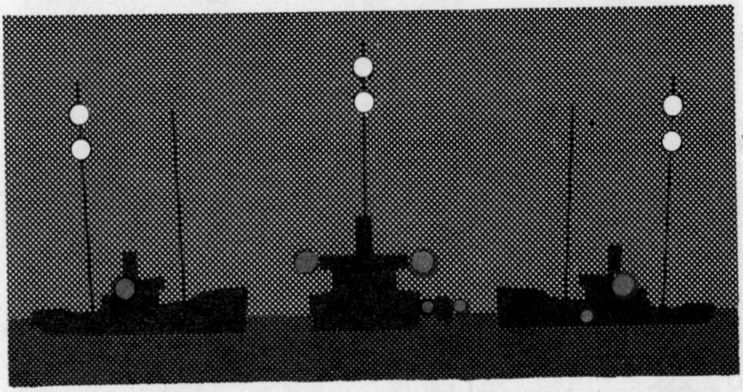

Steam vessel towing another vessel alongside (or pushing her ahead) with towing lights aft. [Inland.]

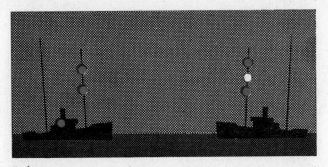

Vessel broken down and not under command under way with way on. [International.]

Vessel not under command due to occupation under way with no way on. [International.]

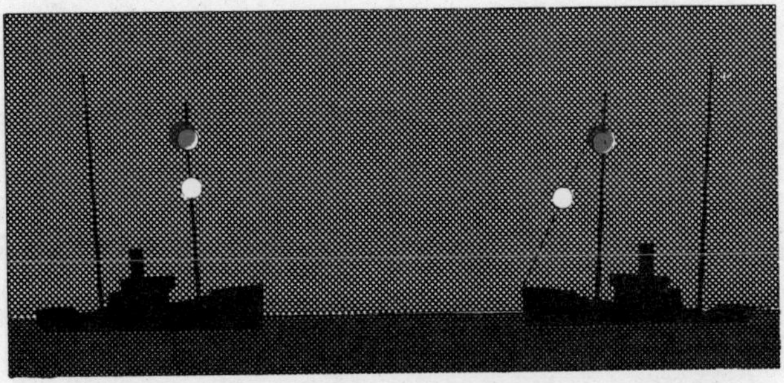

Trawling, dredging, or fishing with drag nets or lines. [Inland.]

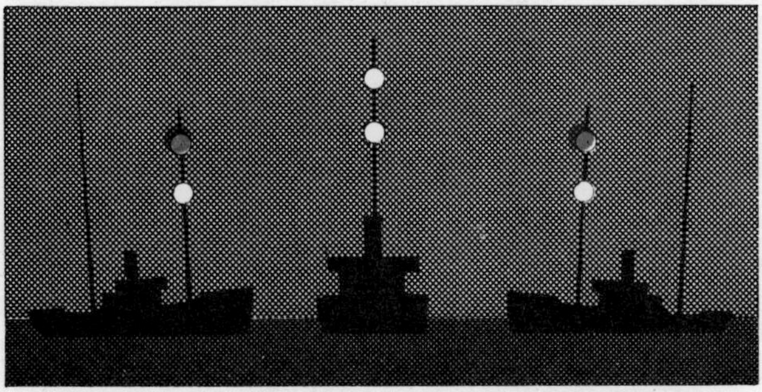

Power-driven trawler. [International.]

SIGNIFICANT CHANGES IN INTERNATIONAL RULES MADE EFECTIVE JANUARY 1, 1954.

In 1948 an International Conference was held in London for the purpose of revising and standardizing the rules governing safety of life at sea. This Conference proposed an extensive revision of the International Rules in effect at that time, which revision became effective January 1, 1954.

The following outline shows briefly the *significant* changes and differences between the present International Rules and the previous International Rules.

DEFINITIONS

Previous Rules	*Rules effective January 1, 1954*
Seaplanes—Not mentioned or covered.	*Seaplanes*—Includes flying boats and any other aircraft designed to maneuver on the water.
Steam vessel	*Power-driven vessel*

LIGHTS AND SHAPES

Range Light

W/20/5 range light, *optional.*	W/20/5 range light, *required* for vessels over 150 ft., optional for vessels under 150 ft. and vessels towing.

Seaplanes

Previous Rules	*Rules effective January 1, 1954*
Not mentioned.	Specifically directed to carry lights similar to those of a vessel of equivalent size and status. This includes towing, aground, anchor, and not under command lights and daymarks. Arcs of visibility of lights rounded off to nearest 10 degrees.

Vessels Fishing

Fishing with drift nets or lines, except trolling lines

2—W/32/3, lower light in direction of gear. Daymark (under way)—a basket. Daymark (at anchor)—a basket to be shown on side which it is safe to pass.	*Gear extending less than 500 ft:* 2—W/32/2, lower light in direction of gear. Daymark (under way)—a basket. Daymark (at anchor)—a basket in direction from anchor ball to gear. *Gear extending more than 500 ft:* 3—W/32/2 in a vertical triangle. Daymark (under way)—a basket forward, plus a black conical shape, apex upward, where it can best be seen. Daymark (at anchor)—same, except that the basket is displayed from the anchor ball towards the gear.

Stern Light

Previous rules	*Rules effective January 1, 1954*
Fixed stern light not required. Any light exhibited in time to avoid collision. If carried fixed, W/12/1.	W/12/2 *required* for vessels under way. Vessels towing or being towed may substitute steering light.

Vessel Laying or Picking Up Telegraph Cable

R over W over R/32/2.	Extended to include a vessel working on an aid to navigation and a vessel unable to maneuver while surveying or engaged in underwater operations. R over W over R/32/2.
Daymark—Red ball over white diamond over red ball.	Daymark—Red ball over white diamond over red ball.

Pilot Vessels

W/32/—at masthead and flareup at intervals not to exceed 15 minutes.	Sailing pilot vessels, W/32/3 at masthead and flareup at intervals not to exceed 10 minutes.
Steam pilot vessel in U.S. waters, W over R/32/2 and flareup at intervals not to exceed 15 minutes.	Power-driven pilot vessels, all waters, W over R/32/3 and flareup at intervals not to exceed 10 minutes. (Intermittent white light may be used for flareup.)

Anchor Lights

Vessel less than 150 ft.

Previous Rules	*Rules effective January 1, 1954*
1—W/32/1.	1—W/32/2.
Daymark—none.	Daymark—one black ball.

Anchor Lights

Vessel of or over 150 Ft.

Previous Rules	*Rules effective January 1, 1954*
2—W/32/1, one high and forward, one low and aft.	2—W/32/3, arranged as before.
Daymark—none.	Daymark—one black ball.

Vessel Aground

Aground in or near a fairway—anchor lights for a vessel of her size, plus 2—R/32/2 in a vertical row.	Aground (*anywhere*). Same as before.
Daymark—none specified.	Daymark—three black balls in vertical row.

Vessel Under Sail and Power

Steam vessel under sail only.	Vessel proceeding under sail *and* machinery.
Daymark—one black ball or shape.	Daymark—one black cone, point up.

FOG SIGNALS

Vessel at Anchor

Previous Rules	*Rules effective January 1, 1954*
Rapid ringing of a bell, five seconds each minute.	Vessel less than 350 ft.—same as before. Vessel greater than 350 ft.: must ring a bell rapidly for 5 seconds each minute in the forepart of the vessel, and immediately thereafter ring a bell or gong of dissimilar tone rapidly for 5 seconds in the after part of the vessel. Vessels at anchor may further indicate their presence and status to approaching vessels by sounding three blasts in succession on the whistle or siren as follows: one-short, one-prolonged, one-short.

Vessel Towing; Not Under Command; Working Telegraph Cable

Prolonged and two short blasts at intervals not to exceed 2 minutes.	Prolonged and two short blasts at intervals not to exceed *1 minute.* Extended to include a vessel working on an aid to navigation or unable to maneuver.

Vessel Towed

Same as vessel towing. Foghorn only. (optional)	Prolonged and three short blasts to be given by the last vessel of a tow, if manned, at intervals not to exceed one minute, on the whistle, siren, or foghorn.

Vessel Aground

Previous rules	*Rules effective January 1, 1954*
Same as for a vessel at anchor.	Same as above for a vessel at anchor, with three sharp and distinct strokes of the bell immediately before and after such signal.

Vessel Fishing

A blast of unspecified length, followed by ringing the bell.	Same as before. May, in lieu of these signals, use a blast consisting of a series of several alternate notes of higher and lower pitch.

STEERING AND SAILING RULES

Aircraft

Not mentioned.	Aircraft on the water are specifically directed to keep clear of all vessels wherever possible. When risk of collision does exist, they conform to the steering and sailing rules as though they were vessels.

Danger Signal

Not included.	Five or more short blasts on the whistle, to be used only by a privileged power-driven vessel in sight of the burdened vessel.

Blind Bend Signal

Not included.	Power-driven vessels approaching a blind bend in a channel must sound one *prolonged* blast on the whistle or siren when ½ mile from such a bend.

INDEX